D1597163

THE ROYAL ABBEY OF SAINT-DENIS

IN THE TIME OF ABBOT SUGER (1122–1151)

THE ROYAL ABBEY OF
SAINT-DENIS

IN THE TIME OF ABBOT SUGER

(1122–1151)

Sumner McKnight Crosby
Jane Hayward
Charles T. Little
William D. Wixom

THE METROPOLITAN MUSEUM OF ART
NEW YORK

The exhibition "The Royal Abbey of Saint-Denis in the Time of Abbot Suger (1122–1151)" has been made possible through the generous support of the Dillon Fund. Under the Arts and Artifacts Indemnity Act, indemnity was granted by the Federal Council on the Arts and Humanities.

This catalogue has been published in conjunction with the exhibition, held at The Cloisters, The Metropolitan Museum of Art, New York, March 31–May 31, 1981.

Library of Congress Cataloging in Publication Data

The Royal Abbey of Saint-Denis in the Time of
   Abbot Suger (1122–1151).

   Exhibition catalog.
   Bibliography: p.
   Includes index.
   1. Art, Gothic—France—Saint-Denis—Exhibitions.
2. Art, French—France—Saint-Denis—Exhibitions.
3. Saint-Denis, France (Benedictine abbey)—Exhibitions.
4. Suger, Abbot of Saint-Denis, 1081–1151.
   I. Crosby, Sumner McKnight, 1909–   II. New York
(City). Metropolitan Museum of Art.
N6851.S29R69   709'.44'362   80-28849
ISBN 0-87099-261-9

Published by The Metropolitan Museum of Art, New York
Bradford D. Kelleher, Publisher
John P. O'Neill, Editor in Chief
Ellen Shultz, Editor
Dana Levy, Designer

Note to the Catalogue:
Although the loans of catalogue numbers 10, 16, 19, and 23 were declined, these objects are discussed and illustrated here because of their importance to the theme of the exhibition. The numbers of these catalogue entries are preceded by an asterisk.

Cover: Chalice of Abbot Suger. See catalogue no. 25

Frontispiece: The Death of Saint Benedict Witnessed by
                Two Monks, from the Saint Benedict window.
                See catalogue no. 17

Contents

Lenders to the Exhibition

Baltimore: Walters Art Gallery

Bryn Athyn, Pennsylvania: The Glencairn Museum,
Academy of the New Church

Cambridge, Massachusetts: Fogg Art Museum, Harvard University

Champs-sur-Marne: Dépôt des Monuments Historiques

London: The British Museum

New York: The Metropolitan Museum of Art

Paris: Monuments Historiques et des Palais Nationaux
Musée de Cluny
Musée du Louvre
Collection Jean Osouf

Saint-Denis: Cathedral of Saint-Denis
Musée Lapidaire
Musée d'Art et d'Histoire

Washington, D.C.: National Gallery of Art

Foreword

The French Revolution not only deposed the monarchy, putting an end to the "ancien régime," but its vengeful fires destroyed literally thousands of châteaux, the symbols—and residences—of the upper classes. The anticlerical wrath of the Revolutionists also brought about the devastation of many churches: sculptured facades were defaced, stained-glass windows shattered, and treasuries ransacked and their contents scattered. Ironically, it was these outrageous acts of the populace and the neglect of the Commune that—almost two hundred years later—would enable The Metropolitan Museum to mount two exhibitions in as many years, presenting the Museum's visitors with major aspects of two of the most glorious monuments of the Gothic period, the cathedral of Notre-Dame de Paris and the Royal Abbey of Saint-Denis (recently designated a cathedral, as well).

The first exhibition was held in the fall of 1979 in the Museum's Medieval galleries and included sculpture from the Early and High Gothic periods that had been forcibly removed from the various portals of Notre-Dame in 1793 and unearthed as recently as 1977 in one of the most dramatic archaeological finds of our time.

The second and present exhibition focuses on the crucible of the Gothic style and on the edifice that represents its first true manifestation, the Abbey of Saint-Denis, as well as on one of the greatest art patrons of the period, Abbot Suger. It was Suger who assembled the craftsmen to rebuild his church, and had fashioned what was to be one of the most important church treasuries in Europe. Even before the Revolution, the Abbey of Saint-Denis, the resting place of the kings of France, was ravaged, and its treasury partially looted and dispersed. Now, for the first time in America, remnants of the abbey's architectural elements and stained glass and examples of Suger's liturgical furnishings and treasury art have been brought together. This collection of works of art is a poignant testimony to the extraordinary artistry of the nascent Gothic style, and scholars may find here the seeds for new research and discoveries.

Indeed, the exhibition, which is being shown at The Cloisters, has been organized to coincide with a major symposium on Saint-Denis, in celebration of the 900th anniversary of the birth of Abbot Suger. The symposium, to be held April 10–12, is sponsored by Columbia University and the International Center of Medieval Art. The catalogue is an indispensable guide to the exhibition and also furnishes the student with a useful handbook to the most salient aspects of Suger's prodigious activity at Saint-Denis. Suger's underlying program for the enlargement and enrichment of the royal abbey, as documented in his writings, is further elaborated upon in these pages in the essays and entries by Sumner

McKnight Crosby, Charles T. Little, Jane Hayward, and by William D. Wixom, who has been the guiding force in organizing this exhibition.

We are indebted to the lenders for their generosity in parting temporarily with some of their finest treasures. I am especially grateful for the essential support of our colleagues and friends here and abroad in facilitating these loans: Hubert Landais, Directeur, Musées de France; C. Pattyn, Directeur du Patrimoine de France; Jean Feray, Inspecteur principal, Monuments Historiques de France; David Wilson, Director, The British Museum; J. Carter Brown, Director, National Gallery of Art, Washington, D.C.; Richard H. Randall, Jr., Director, Walters Art Gallery; Seymour Slive, Director, Fogg Art Museum; Lachlan Pitcairn, Secretary, The Glencairn Foundation; Reverend Martin Pryke, Director, The Glencairn Museum, Academy of the New Church; and Monsieur and Madame Jean Osouf.

Our warm appreciation is also due to the many other people whose names appear in the list of acknowledgments that follows. I especially thank our staff members for all their efforts toward making this event a reality.

This exhibition would not have been possible without the generous support of the Dillon Fund. Under the Arts and Artifacts Indemnity Act, indemnity was granted by the Federal Council on the Arts and Humanities.

Philippe de Montebello
Director

Acknowledgments

FRANCE

Irène Aghion
Conservateur, Cabinet des Médailles, Bibliothèque Nationale

Pierre-Marie Auzas
Inspecteur général, Monuments Historiques de France

Françoise Baron
Conservateur, Département des Sculptures, Musée du Louvre

Alain Erlande-Brandenburg
Conservateur en chef, Musée de Cluny

Catherine Brisac
Adjointe à la conservation, Musée des Plans-Reliefs

Jean-René Gaborit
Conservateur en chef, Département des Sculptures, Musée du Louvre

Danielle Gaborit-Chopin
Conservateur, Département des Objets d'art, Musée du Louvre

Marie-Madeleine Gauthier
Directeur, Laboratoire de recherche sur l'émaillerie médiévale,
Centre national de la Recherche scientifique

Louis Grodecki
Professeur émérite, Sorbonne

Jean-Jacques Gruber
Président, Chambre syndicale des Maîtres Verriers

Denis Lavalle
Inspecteur, Monuments Historiques de France

Jean Rollin
Conservateur, Musée d'Art et d'Histoire, Saint-Denis

Maurice Soucheyre
Maire-adjoint, Chargé des affaires culturelles, Saint-Denis

Élisabeth Taburet
Conservateur, Musée de Cluny

GREAT
BRITAIN

John Cherry
Assistant Keeper, The British Museum

Neil Stratford
Keeper of Medieval and Later Antiquities, The British Museum

UNITED
STATES

Dr. Lynus Barnes
Research Chemist, National Bureau of Standards

Pamela Z. Blum
Assistant Professor, Columbia University

Dr. Robert H. Brill
Research Scientist, The Corning Museum of Glass

Diana Brouillette
Assistant Professor, Vassar College

Elizabeth Brown
Professor, Brooklyn College

William Clark
Professor, Queens College

Victor Covey
Chief Conservator, National Gallery of Art, Washington, D.C.

Stephen Gardner
Assistant Professor, Columbia University

Paula Gerson
Chairman, Suger Symposium

Douglas Lewis
Curator of Sculpture, National Gallery of Art, Washington, D.C.

Gabrielle Spiegel
Associate Professor, University of Maryland

Harvey Stahl
Associate Professor, University of California at Berkeley

THE
METROPOLITAN
MUSEUM
OF ART

Barbara Drake Boehm
Senior Administrative Assistant, Department of Medieval Art

Katharine R. Brown
Senior Research Associate, Department of Medieval Art

John Buchanan
Registrar

Suse Childs
Assistant Museum Librarian, The Cloisters

Jeffrey Daly
Chief Designer

Carmen Gómez-Moreno
Curator, Department of Medieval Art

Aphrodite Hagigeorgiou
Former Senior Administrative Assistant, The Cloisters

Deborah Kraak
Graduate Intern, The Cloisters

Timothy Husband
Associate Curator, The Cloisters

Carl Koivuniemi
Administrative Assistant, The Cloisters

Nancy Kueffner
Associate Museum Educator, The Cloisters

Dana Levy
Designer, exhibition catalogue

Allison Merrill
Assistant, Department of Medieval Art

Herbert M. Moskowitz
Associate Registrar

Kathleen Nolan
J. Clawson Mills Fellow, Department of Medieval Art

John P. O'Neill
Editor in Chief and General Manager of Publications, Editorial
Department

Ellen Shultz
Editor, Editorial Department

John B. Sinclair
Building Supervisor, The Cloisters

For bright is that which is brightly coupled with the bright,

And bright is the noble edifice which is pervaded by the new light;

Which stands enlarged in our time,

I, who was Suger, being the leader while it was being accomplished.

Suger, *De Administratione*, XXIX, ed. and trans. Panofsky, 1979, 51

Figure 1. Abbot Suger, in the Annunciation panel from the Infancy of Christ window. c. 1144. Choir, Chapel of the Virgin

Abbot Suger, the Abbey of Saint-Denis, and the New Gothic Style

The history of the Abbey of Saint-Denis is a long one, with many bright moments, but certainly none was brighter than the period of its rebuilding in the twelfth century under its illustrious abbot, Suger (fig. 1).[1] Suger's workmen must be credited with creating a new style, the Gothic style, which dominated western Europe for almost three centuries. Volumes have been written about Saint-Denis (fig. 2), but we are still searching out the secrets that made it such a creative environment in the twelfth century.

Although Saint Denis, the first Bishop of Paris, was apparently martyred in the mid-third century, and the site of his burial in the village of Catulliacum, now the suburb of Saint-Denis, attracted special veneration from that time on, it was not until the sixth century that the first royal burial took place there, and not until the seventh century that the generosity of King Dagobert I and his son Clovis II gave the religious community its monastic standing and endowed it with the properties and particular privileges that were to make it one of the powerful institutions in Medieval France.[2] Rebuilt as one of the very first great Carolingian abbeys—a new church was dedicated in the presence of Charlemagne and his court on February 24, 775—it became a royal abbey when Charles the Bald in 867 assumed the title of lay abbot in order to give it every possible protection as the successive Norman raids disturbed the security of northern and central France. Saint Denis by this time had long been recognized as the patron saint of the monarchy, and the fairs held under the abbey's aegis were also renowned throughout western Europe. After Hugh Capet,

Figure 2. West facade. c. 1135–40

Figure 3. Reconstruction by
Sumner McK. Crosby of the west
facade, as it would have appeared
when completed. Drawing by
Gregory Robeson

14

who was buried in the abbey church in 996, only three of the French kings—Philip I, Louis VII, and Louis XI—were to be buried elsewhere.

In the twelfth century the abbey buildings, which had been in active use since the eighth century, were in obvious need of repair and renovation. Suger, who became abbot of Saint-Denis in 1122, wrote that the old church had "come to suffer grave inconveniences. Often on feast days, completely filled, it disgorged through all its doors the excess of the crowds as they moved in opposite directions, and the outward pressure of the foremost ones not only prevented those attempting to enter from entering but also expelled those who had already entered."[3]

Suger's biographer, Willelmus, wondered how so much spirit, such beauty, such greatness, could be contained in such a frail little body.[4] Part of Suger's epitaph read:

> Small of body and family, constrained by twofold smallness,
> He refused, in his smallness, to be a small man.[5]

In spite of his frailty and his very humble beginnings, Suger is one of the most important men in French history. An able administrator and an acute businessman, he was also a loyal advisor and intimate friend of both Louis VI and Louis VII. During the Second Crusade he was a Regent of France and was proclaimed *pater patriae* before his death in 1151, when he was seventy years old. He was also one of the first Medieval historians, and during the rebuilding of the abbey proved to be an outstanding patron of the arts. Yet his life was spent as a monk and abbot. At the age of ten he was given to Saint-Denis as an oblate and from his early years was profoundly grateful to the church that had nurtured him. Two primary goals seem to have dominated his vision: stable central authority in both secular and spiritual affairs to be achieved by a strong monarchy and a respected Papacy, and an opportunity to glorify the Church, which he proposed to do by embellishing his own abbey so that it might shine as an example to all others, excelling even the glories of Constantinople.

We must not overlook the importance of Abbot Suger's administrative and financial skills in contributing to the achievement of his new church. In his account of his administration he mentions in detail how he trebled and quadrupled the revenues of many of the abbey's feudal holdings. With considerable relish he tells of how he was offered mutton by Cistercian monks for the great feasts at the time of consecration, how his own perseverance led to the discovery of the large beams that were necessary for the roof of the new building, how "so many [gems and pearls] were brought to us for sale from nearly all parts of the world (and, by the grace of God, we were also offered wherewith to buy them) that we should have been unable to let them go without great shame and offense to the Saints."[6] We can judge his astuteness in acquiring some of the precious jewels for altar decorations by his account of how he encouraged prelates who were present at the laying of the foundation stones of the new choir to place their jewels in the mortar as they chanted: "All thy walls are precious stones."[7] At that time, we should remember, the mortar did not set for many days, even weeks or months. The same chapter of his account of the consecrations of his new building specifies in considerable detail exactly which funds were to be reserved for the completion of the work, and, in an Ordinance signed in 1140 or 1141, he carefully enumerated the funds to be devoted to the welfare of the abbey and its monks.[8]

It was this scrupulous attention to detail that made possible the rapid progress of his building campaigns and assured the presence of the most competent workmen and artists. Suger knew where the best workmen and the most original artists were to be found, for he had traveled through

Figure 4. Narthex, showing the
diagonally centered southeast pier,
as seen from the northwest.
Begun c. 1135

much of western Europe and, unquestionably, had visited many of the active workshops. Four different times he made the long trip to Italy, twice to attend Lateran synods in Rome and twice to confer with Pope Calixtus II; and twice he went south into Apulia, visiting Monte Cassino, Bari, and Bitonto. He also knew southern and southwestern France, having been sent to Montpellier in 1118 to meet Pope Gelasius II, and Suger accompanied the young Louis VII to his meeting with Eleanor of Aquitaine in Bordeaux and attended their marriage in Poitiers in 1137. Early in his career he lived in Normandy, for his first administrative position in 1107 was that of prior at the monastery of Berneval on the Channel coast, northeast of Fécamp. Later, he accompanied Pope Innocent II to Rouen, and it is possible that he went as far as Liège in Belgium during the same trip with the pope in 1131. He must have seen the great cathedrals of the Rhineland as well, for he attended the Reichstag at Mainz in 1125. In other words, except for England, Germany beyond the Rhineland, and Spain, there are definite records of his travels to or through most of the regions where the Romanesque style was more actively practiced. He must have studied with his own eyes the newest Romanesque abbeys with their richly carved portals and capitals. When, about 1135, he decided to begin the building of the massive new entrance to the church at Saint-Denis, he knew where to seek out the best talents available. He could and did call, as he recorded, artists from many regions. His reputation as an able administrator and enthusiastic abbot made the proposition to participate an attractive one.

Even while still a pupil, Suger had wished to be able to renovate the old church. When finally, as abbot, he had the opportunity, he was faced with an unexpected obstruction. A popular legend recounted that the old church, which was believed to have been built by Dagobert, had been consecrated by Christ himself and a crowd of angels on the eve of its consecration by the clergy. This miraculous event, of course, endowed the building—and indeed every stone with which it was built—with the veneration due a relic. Such venerability proved more effective in those days than any number of historic-preservation groups would today and Suger was forced to build his new church piecemeal, beginning at the western entrance and then moving to the eastern end to erect his splendid new choir, leaving the old nave and transept standing between the two. The great western entrance with its three sculptured portals—including column statues closely resembling those of the Royal Portal at Chartres Cathedral, and the rose window—was consecrated on June 9, 1140.[9] Although only one of the towers that surmounted the western mass of the structure was finished in Suger's lifetime, this "westwerke," with its three upper chapels, dominated the plains north of Paris as a symbol of royal power and a Church militant.

Order in the temporal realm dominates this first building campaign.[10] The facade at Saint-Denis is not just an exterior embellishment. The twin towers, developed to such a degree by Norman masons, are not flush with the plane of the facade but are set back on the mass of the entrance bays so that they become an integral part of the whole western section of the church (fig. 3). Such a western mass or westwork was introduced into ecclesiastical architecture in Carolingian times and was further developed in the Ottonian imperial basilicas of the tenth and eleventh centuries in the Rhine Valley. The westwork was the symbol of secular, royal authority, as distinct from the authority of the clergy, who presided over the church at the opposite or eastern end.

An unusual feature at Saint-Denis today is the presence of crenellations crowning the top of the facade. Though rebuilt, they were mentioned by Suger as part of the original design. Similar crenellations over gateways

Figure 5. Exterior view of the choir, with the chapels and crypt constructed under Suger's abbacy

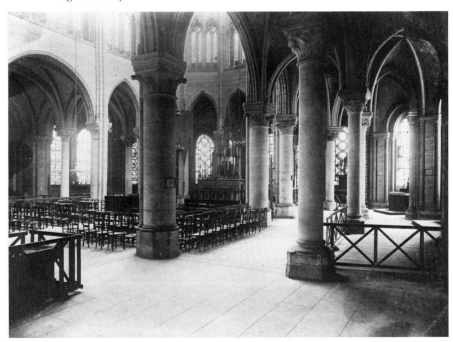

Figure 6. Interior view of the choir, as seen from the south aisle

can be traced back to antiquity and are present in early images of the Temple of Solomon. At Saint-Denis, they remind us that the patron saint was protector of the monarchy and that the church guarded the royal crowns and the Banner of Saint Denis (see pages 103–4).

Directly below the crenellations is the rose window, the first one, to our knowledge, to appear as an integral element in the design of a western facade of a church, but a form that would dominate Gothic architecture throughout history. At Saint-Denis the rose opened into a central upper chapel in the western part of the structure, where it could also be seen from the eastern choir. Such a circular, solar disc was added to the wall of the western apse at Worms, another of the Rhenish imperial basilicas. There it framed the emperor when he sat on his throne at the western end of the nave.

Among the many "new" features of the portals at Saint-Denis are the three arched openings immediately adjacent to each other. The image of three arches, with the central one larger than the side ones, recalls the famous Roman triumphal arch of Constantine, or the one at Orange in the Rhone Valley, both of which Suger must have seen on his travels. Roman writers have described the triumphant emperor—and his legions—passing through the arch as an act of purification and cleansing on his way to be received as a divinity in his heavenly city. This concept of the emperor's divine relation to the deity was reiterated by the Ottonian emperors of the tenth and eleventh centuries. Yet, in spite of all of these analogies, Suger, in his writings, explicitly stated that the three portals represented the Trinity.

Flanking each of the three portals were column statues, figures of Old Testament kings and queens that are thought to be the royal ancestors of Christ. Diagonally placed in the splays of the portals, these column figures echo the diagonally centered narthex piers inside the western part of the structure (fig. 4). The piers comprise clusters of colonnettes, each of which articulates an arch or rib of the vault above, thus heralding the lucidity of nascent Gothic architecture. The column statues of the portals were another innovation at Saint-Denis that was to continue in Gothic art. It is thought that they refer to regnum et sacerdotium, or the secular and spiritual realms. The presence of royalty, prominently displayed on the entrance portals, was certainly appropriate at the royal abbey, and the emphasis upon secular and spiritual authority was a basic premise in Suger's philosophy. These figures reiterate the balance of authority and emphasize the position of the Christian Church in its terrestrial world.

The Saint-Denis choir to the east was begun on July 13, 1140, and was finished in the remarkably short time of three years and three months (fig. 5). Its dedication took place on June 14, 1144, in the presence of King Louis VII, Eleanor of Aquitaine, and a multitude of archbishops, bishops, abbots, and other dignitaries.[11] This choir, with its nine adjoining chapels open to the entire church by an audacious use of a relatively new structural device, the rib-vault, and lit by the sixteen great stained-glass windows, whose colored beams of light were reflected from the bright tesserae of the mosaic floors and the gold, enameled, and jeweled decorations of the altars, was the first truly Gothic structure (fig. 6). It must have amazed and delighted Suger's contemporaries, who returned to their own domains eager to emulate his example. Within the next thirty years most of the Early Gothic cathedrals of the Île-de-France had been begun and a new style proclaimed that was so unlike anything from the past that it was called opus modernum, modern architecture, and so French that it came to be known as opere francigena.[12] It was not until the fifteenth century that the new humanists, men of the Renaissance, dubbed it barbarian and called it Gothic.[13]

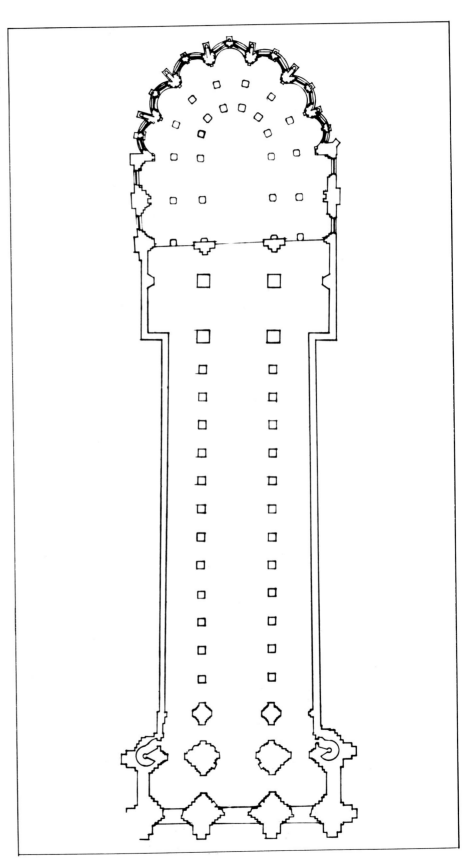

Figure 7. Plan of Suger's narthex and choir attached to the Carolingian nave and transept. After Sumner McK. Crosby

The celestial hierarchy, the realm of light, and the verities of sacred literature were given material existence in this second building campaign. The contrast between the symbolism of the western bays and that of the eastern choir is the difference between literal exposition and intuitive response. In the entrance bays, the actual forms of the architecture—the crenellations, circular window, and arched doorways with images carved in stone—invite specific interpretations. In the choir, it is the environment created by the architecture and the emotional reaction to colored light and to bright, shining surfaces that evoke abstract, metaphysical responses—the distinction between the material world of our physical, terrestrial, and cognitive experience, and the immaterial universe of celestial hierarchies. Suger's writings reflect this difference. He describes the placing of gems in the new foundation, likening the abbey to the City of God. He speaks of the dedication of the new choir, with the prelates arranged in ecclesiastical order, as a reflection of the hierarchies of the celestial order. Suger's master mason proved his genius by constructing this "crown of light," these adjacent chapels open to one another and illuminated by large stained-glass windows.

The striking contrast at Saint-Denis between the crypt and the choir above it demonstrates vividly the difference between Romanesque and Gothic construction. Both levels have exactly the same plan; indeed, the crypt functions as the foundation for the choir. But the structure contrasts the solidity of mural construction—groin vaulting, enclosed volumes, and reflected light—in the crypt with the diaphanous construction—minimal support, articulated skeletal rib-vaults, and the maximal introduction of refracted colored light—in the choir. Historians of architecture know no prototype for Suger's new choir. To the abbot and his contemporaries its "beauty" was enhanced by the "costly vessels" and other decorations made for the choir, which—with its luminous windows and gem-encrusted ornaments—Suger clearly intended to be "neither of the slime of this earth nor entirely of the purity of heaven," a material, celestial Jerusalem, an earthly abode of God, which would encourage the mind to move from the material to the immaterial.

Suger was immensely proud of his new church, which he hoped that his successors would complete if he himself could not (fig. 7). I believe that he intended that the new transept and nave would symbolically signify the successful joining of the terrestrial to the celestial realms by the Papacy. Our excavations in the transepts and nave show that work was started on both the north and the south sides of the church, as a sort of envelope around the old, eighth-century building. Neither side progressed very far, so that the old nave remained standing until it was replaced by the present structure in the thirteenth century. Enough remains to prove that the new nave was to be two meters wider on both sides than the old one, but that the old bay width—four meters from center to center—would be maintained, as would the width of the nave, even though work on the interior of the new nave was never begun. The proportions of the side aisles, four meters by eight meters, as well as the presence of the ambulatory and radiating chapels in the choir, are adequate proof that double side aisles on each side of the nave were planned by Suger's master mason.

The recent discovery of bases carved for the new nave—but used only to shore up the foundations of the thirteenth-century crossing—prove that columns, not piers, would have been the supports. A colonnaded nave with double side aisles was a distinguishing feature of Old Saint Peter's in Rome. Although we cannot prove that Suger had such a reference in mind, it is true that the great third church at Cluny had double side aisles, as did Saint-Sernin in Toulouse, and that in both instances allegiance only to Rome was a major element in their existence. It may not be too much of an exaggeration to suggest that Suger's new nave was to have been an explicit reference to the Papacy as a juncture between the terrestrial *regnum* of the western bays and the celestial *sacerdotium* of the choir.

Almost every technique was vigorously pursued at Saint-Denis, and all of the building crafts, including stone carving, were, of course, actively engaged. Suger's writings describe the work of ivory carvers, metalworkers, and experts in stained glass, as well as mosaicists, and he even speaks of an "increase in very good textiles"[14] during his administration. In all likelihood, these textiles were purchased, although it is possible that embroiderers or other experts were on hand for their repair and upkeep. Scribes must have been busy keeping accounts and copying manuscripts for the abbey's priories. Although specific examples are difficult to identify, most scholars agree that manuscripts must have been decorated and illustrated by skilled illuminators and miniaturists in the Saint-Denis workshops. Only recently it has been proposed that "the new style . . . which owed so much to stained glass . . . was formed in a milieu which resembled, and may perhaps have been identical with, the royal abbey."[15]

The fact that Suger described the building of the church and his personal involvement in its completion has led many to call him the architect. There is no need to deny Suger his enthusiasm or determination to build a great, new church, but we have no evidence, even in his own writings, that he served as an apprentice mason. The man, or men, responsible for the precocious use of the rib-vaults in the choir, as well as for the choir's original plan, could not have been what we would call amateurs. The same is true of the intricate, unprecedented symbolism of the scenes in the three portals of the west facade, in the windows, on the altars, or on the Great Cross. Suger was well-read for his day, and he certainly had a bright, active mind, but he must have consulted his monks, who had more time for theology and scholarly endeavors, and engaged their assistance in developing the iconographic themes and their complicated interrelationships. Suger seems to have been one of those truly great patrons who could attract the outstanding talents of his time to work for him. He was even more astute in the degree to which he must have left them to their own devices. His good management provided the funds for large numbers of workmen and artists, as well as for the most costly materials. His bold aspirations encouraged excited responses. The result was Saint-Denis and the Gothic style. We cannot reconstruct in every detail what Suger's accomplishments at Saint-Denis actually were, but we are able to appreciate the intensity of his vision, his extraordinary energies, and the wisdom that he displayed as he brought together his international workshop and encouraged it to create a new style.

Sumner McKnight Crosby
Professor Emeritus
Yale University
New Haven, Connecticut

Notes

1. I thank the editors of the *Journal of World History* for permission to quote sections from my article "An International Workshop in the Twelfth Century," published in vol. X, no. 1, 1966, 19–30, of their journal.

2. Félibien, 1706, contains the documents and legends of the history of the abbey. My volume (1942) treats the development of the abbey and its buildings before Suger began their rebuilding.

3. *De Consecratione*, II, ed. Panofsky, 1979, 87.

4. Lecoy de la Marche, 1867, 378; "...quod in tam brevi corpusculo talem natura collocaverit animum, tam formosum, tam magnum."

5. Panofsky, 1979, 33. Panofsky's introductory essay on Suger is most perceptive. See also Cartellieri, 1898; Aubert and Beaulieu, 1950; Crosby, 1953, chap. III; von Simson, 1962, chap. 3.

6. *De Consecratione*, V, ed. Panofsky, 1979, 107.

7. *De Consecratione*, IV, ed. Panofsky, 1979, 103.

8. *Ordinatio*, ed. Panofsky, 1979, 122–37.

9. Suger records the inscription that he had engraved on the western doors: "Annus millenus et centenus quadragenus/Annus erat Verbi, quando sacrata fuit" ("The year was the One Thousand, One Hundred, and Fortieth/Year of the Word when [this structure] was consecrated"), *De Administratione*, XXVII, ed. Panofsky, 1979, 46–47. Later, when speaking of the laying of the foundations for the choir, on July 13, 1140, he mentions using the water that had been consecrated for the dedication of the western portions of the church, five days before the Ides of June; see *De Consecratione*, IV, ed. Panofsky, 1979, 103. The precise dating of the work at Saint-Denis is another reason why Suger's building is so important, since few other twelfth-century structures can be so securely and accurately dated.

10. Material on the iconographic concept of Suger's building program at Saint-Denis is drawn from my paper, "Abbot Suger's Program for His New Abbey Church," read at the Monasticism and the Arts Symposium, Yale University, Spring 1980. An edited version will appear in a forthcoming publication of these papers.

11. Suger gives all these details in *De Consecratione*, VI, ed. Panofsky, 1979, 110–15.

12. Branner, Robert, *St. Louis and the Court Style in Gothic Architecture*, London, 1965, 7.

13. Frankl, 1960, 259–60.

14. *De Administratione*, I, [XXXIV A], ed. Panofsky, 1979, 41, 81.

15. Porcher, 1959, 45.

Monumental Sculpture at Saint-Denis Under the Patronage of Abbot Suger

The West Facade

On June 9, 1140, Abbot Suger dedicated the west end of the Abbey Church of Saint-Denis in the presence of the Archbishop of Rouen and several bishops. In spite of his detailed description of the gilt-bronze doors (now lost) of the main entrance he made only elliptical references to the decoration of the portals. On the left portal he had a mosaic affixed to the tympanum that, he says, was "contrary to modern custom," and he had the lintel of the central portal inscribed with the verse: "Receive, O stern Judge, the prayers of Thy Suger;/Grant that I be mercifully numbered among Thy own sheep."[1] Neither the mosaic nor the inscription have survived.

The triple portals that unify the west facade contain a rich and innovative sculptural program and, despite the losses and excessive restorations of the eighteenth and nineteenth centuries, we can reconstruct Suger's intentions for the iconographic program and thus evaluate his achievements (figs. 8, 9). The central portal is dominated by the theme of the Last Judgment, the first instance of the representation of that subject on the facade of a church in northern France (fig. 10). Although the Last Judgment according to the Gospel of Saint Matthew occurred previously on churches in the south of France at Beaulieu and Conques, neither is a direct iconographic source for the portal at Saint-Denis.[2] On the central axis an oversized figure of the enthroned Christ as Judge is depicted with his arms outstretched in front of a cross, holding two scrolls with inscriptions that are taken from Matthew (25:34, 41). Immediately to Christ's right and left are the Virgin and possibly Saint John the Evangelist in the company of the apostles, who converse *in disputatione* as in the Apostles Relief (cat. no. 6). If it is, in fact, Saint John who is shown with the Virgin—both functioning as intercessors for mankind—then this is the first time they appear together as an integral part of a Last Judgment program. In the zone below is the Resurrection of the Dead, among whom is the restored but iconographically authentic figure of Suger in supplication at the feet of Christ.

From the tympanum the program extends outward into the archivolts. In the first archivolt are themes related to the act of judgment: to the left are the Saved, within the Gates of Paradise; just above are children held in the bosom of Abraham; to the right are scenes of the Damned. In the second, third, and fourth archivolts are the twenty-four seated Elders of the Apocalypse, holding vials and musical instruments. Those in the outer range are seated within a continuous vine branch, an apparent

25

Figure 8. West facade portals

reference to the theme of the Tree of Jesse. On the central axis of the outer two archivolts is the Trinity, with the dove of the Holy Ghost above a bust of God the Father holding a medallion of the Paschal Lamb, a reference to the Apocalyptic Vision. Consequently, the most significant ideas are presented on the central axis of the portal. The doorjambs also contain a feature not previously introduced in sculptural programs on portals: the parable of the Wise and Foolish Virgins (Matthew 25:1–12), an allegorical elaboration of the theme of the tympanum, the open and closed doors to Salvation. Thus, the central portal is formally organized into interlocking zones of sculpture in which the Last Judgment is represented with an entirely new iconographic clarity and a harmony that made it the prototype for succeeding Gothic portals.

The lateral portals have suffered from severe and often more distorting restoration than the central portal. The tympanum over the right doorway shows the communion of Saint Denis and his companions, Rusticus and Eleutherius, with Christ administering the Eucharist to Saint Denis. Although the outer archivolt is a nineteenth-century fabrication, the inner one dates from the twelfth century and is iconographically valid. Of particular significance is the devotion of a portal program on the west facade of a church to its patron saint, a feature adopted on most later Gothic cathedrals. The doorjambs of the right portal contain a cycle of the Labors of the Months, with the first six months in ascending order on the right side and those from July to December in descending order on the left. The Signs of the Zodiac cycle roughly parallels this arrangement, but it is located on the doorposts of the left portal. Between them the two cycles encompass the terrestrial and cosmological aspects of the universe, linking the iconography on the two lateral portals. Whether the left portal originally displayed a similar thematic unity extending from the tympanum to the archivolt is uncertain, since it is not known if the present nineteenth-century tympanum showing Saint Denis and his companions being led to prison is an echo of the lost composition of the mosaic erected by Suger.[3] The subject of the twice-restored second archivolt is equally enigmatic.

The most dramatic innovation in the design of Suger's new facade was the conspicuous representation of biblical kings, queens, patriarchs, and prophets in the form of column statues flanking each of the three portals. Originally twenty column statues adorned the facade: eight flanking the central portal and six on each of the lateral entrances. Engravings of these

26

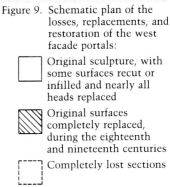

Figure 9. Schematic plan of the losses, replacements, and restoration of the west facade portals:

☐ Original sculpture, with some surfaces recut or infilled and nearly all heads replaced

▧ Original surfaces completely replaced, during the eighteenth and nineteenth centuries

┌─┐ Completely lost sections
└─┘

figures were published by Dom Bernard de Montfaucon (1729) before the removal of the statues in 1771 (fig. 11). Four heads (cat. nos. 3A–D), which have been identified by their close correspondence to the drawings made for Montfaucon, are all that remain of these imposing sculptures.[4]

Both the meaning and the prototypes for the column statues continue to puzzle scholars. Most of the figures represent queens and kings of the Old Testament, and they have been interpreted as the royal ancestors of Christ, or as a horizontal Tree of Jesse, but the arrangement is not in a strict genealogical sequence.[5] Although others are patriarchs and prophets, only one can be identified by his attribute: Moses is shown holding the tablets of the Law. The incorporation of a royal theme on the facade of the royal abbey may be regarded as an expression in monumental terms of the idea of Merovingian-Capetian kingship fused with a Christological-biblical order.[6] As a unified series, the column statues thus exemplified the spiritual ancestors of the French kings. Both physically and programmatically, these column statues form the foundations of the three archivolts and, as such, reveal a meaningful relationship particularly evident in the central portal of the Last Judgment. If the column statues are vehicles for extending downward the iconographic program of the tympanum and archivolts, their identity may be a direct function of the theme depicted above.[7] They, therefore, unify and amplify the overall meaning of the portals.

In spite of the enormous impact of the column statues, their formal sources continue to be a mystery. Indeed, almost simultaneously with those at Saint-Denis, nascent statues emerging from piers do occur on portals at Ferrara (c. 1135) and Verona (c. 1139), and on column supports for arcades or altars in Tuscany, such as at San Giorgio Brancoli.[8] Furthermore, the clustering of figures around a portal, primarily as overblown reliefs, is found on the facades of Vézelay, Moissac, and Santiago de Compostela, but even these do not operate functionally or iconographically in the same way as the statues at Saint-Denis, which, therefore, appear to have no direct prototypes. The Saint-Denis column statues became the key unifying factor in the layout of a portal, systematically linking the stepped dado, capital frieze, and archivolts into a visually coherent architectural and sculptural system. This more-integrated approach to the decoration of the portal was immediately adopted on the west facade at Chartres, and even migrated quickly to England—to Colchester and Lincoln—probably before 1146.[9] Thus, the Saint-Denis col-

27

Figure 10. Last Judgment portal. c. 1135–40

umn statues form an integral part of a new concept of facade decoration that directly affected church design through the Gothic period.

A full assessment of the style of the sculpture on the facade is restricted by its condition and state of restoration. Only recently have scholars begun to determine which sculpture is original.[10] However, after studying the illustrations published by Montfaucon and those parts of the portals that have been established as unrestored, one may distinguish the styles of at least three different ateliers of sculptors working on the facade decoration. The stylistic differences among them—in the proportion of the figures, the treatment of the drapery, and the articulation of the faces—reflect different traditions whose identities are still unclear. Nevertheless, there is an overall uniformity of the sculptural vocabulary that was achieved primarily by means of a unity and integration of composition and plan. It was the inventiveness and richness of the forms and iconography that began to signify a new epoch in Medieval sculpture. Sculptural volumes seem to have been consciously modulated in relation to the distance at which they would be viewed by the spectator, with less relief projection in the doorposts and lower tympana and archivolts. With the exception of the heads of the column statues, the volumes are more intensified in the upper portions of the tympana and archivolts, producing a strong visual effect. There is an emphasis on modeling and a tendency toward more naturalistic proportions. The result is a new order and equilibrium of forms, which have a directness and vigor without the agitation and deformity so characteristic of Romanesque art. In essence, the Saint-Denis sculpture is the first harbinger of the Gothic style.

The impact of the design, iconography, and style of the west facade at Saint-Denis on the first generation of Gothic architecture was not adopted wholesale, but, rather, selectively. At Chartres, some ten years later, there is evidence of the direct adaptation of only some parts of the sculptural cycle at Saint-Denis, mainly in the type of dress represented, and in the richly decorated colonnettes. Inexplicable is the apparent fact that many of the major monuments of northern France—at Angers, Le Mans, Corbeil, Étampes, Notre-Dame in Paris, Saint-Loup-de-Naud— have more direct links with the sculpture at Chartres than with Saint-Denis. Even though these monuments have assimilated the key ideas of Saint-Denis, which produced the mutations significant for the Gothic style, the specific role of Saint-Denis in the context of Early Gothic sculpture leaves many questions unanswered.

The Cloister

Just as he omits any discussion of sculpture on the west facade of Saint-Denis, Abbot Suger is also silent about the cloister. Documentation concerning the cloister derives primarily from Montfaucon's engravings (1729), based upon drawings by Antoine Benoist, which included "two statues of Merovingian Kings with nimbi, sculptured on two columns supporting the cloister...in the oldest part of the cloister of the Monastery of Saint-Denis."[11] The Metropolitan king—first identified by Vera Ostoia[12] with one of the column statues reproduced by Montfaucon, and said to have come from the old cloister—is the only complete column figure from the abbey to survive (fig. 17). Its original position within the old cloister is uncertain, since it was reintegrated into the remodeled thirteenth-century cloister. Accounts from the year 1287 refer to the "washing and repainting of images in the cloister," and in 1294 there were expenses for "repairs of ancient prophets." The appearance of this cloister is known from a late-seventeenth-century engraving in Dom

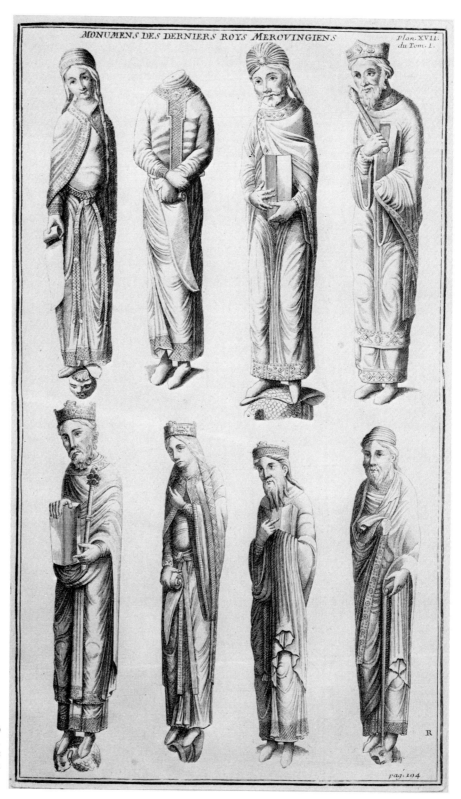

Figure 11. Engraving of the lost jamb statues from the Last Judgment portal. 1729. After Dom Bernard de Montfaucon

Michel Germain's *Monasticon Gallicanum*, made before the cloister was dismantled about 1771 (fig. 12).[13] In 1774, this column figure was inventoried and sold to the Marquis de Migieu, who removed it to his château in Burgundy,[14] where it was recorded again in 1785.[15]

The cloister of Saint-Denis was probably one of the earliest in northern France to be decorated with column figures, but this idea possibly had a precedent at Saint-Bertrand-de-Comminges, where there is a column *in situ* representing Luke and Matthew,[16] and at the monastery of San Pelayo de Antealtares, Santiago de Compostela, where there is a multi-figured column dating from the second quarter of the twelfth century, which certainly comes from a cloister.[17] The thirteenth-century remodeling of the Saint-Denis cloister may not have affected the function or location of the column statues, and it is possible that they were linked to the chapter house, an integral part of the cloister. The concept of placing column statues at the entrance to the chapter house must have been a common feature of northern French cloisters during the twelfth century. However, only one survives *in situ*: to the right of the entrance to the Abbey of Saint-Georges-de-Boscherville (Normandy), dating from about 1170, stands a single group of three column statues.[18] A mid-twelfth-century fragment of a column statue, possibly from the cloister of the Abbey of Saint-Bertin, is in the local museum at Saint-Omer and another complete one from Saint-Maur-des-Fossés, depicting Saint Michael, is at Dumbarton Oaks.[19] These early examples set the stage for the decoration of the cloister of Notre-Dame-en-Vaux at Châlons-sur-Marne, the most ambitious program of its kind that is known to us.

The column figures from the cloister appear to have played a significant role in the development of Early Gothic sculpture. The king (cat. no. 4) displays some stylistic affinities with the contemporary sculpture of the headmaster on the west facade at Chartres (c. 1145–55) in the strict axial relationship between the statue and the colonnette, the drapery pattern, and the modeling of the surface.[20] Although the facade sculpture at Saint-Denis is demonstrably earlier than Chartres, the cloister appears to be exactly parallel in time. A date of about 1150 can be supported by several Burgundian connections. The cloister sculpture is stylistically similar to the sculpture from the portals (now destroyed) at Saint-Bénigne in Dijon—a relationship first recognized in the eighteenth century.[21] Now thought to date from about 1160 at the earliest, the Dijon portal was influenced primarily by the Saint-Denis cloister and to a lesser extent by Chartres Cathedral.[22] In addition, a small undated fragment of a standing figure in Vézelay,[23] whose drapery is almost identical to that of this king and to figures at Chartres, seems to reinforce the notion that the influence extended to, rather than away from, Burgundy. This mid-century date is further supported by the capitals with harpies, originally in the cloister (cat. no. 5B; fig. 18), which appear more advanced in style and which correspond to identical capitals, dated after 1144 and before 1163, in the choir of Saint-Germain-des-Prés, Paris. If the cloister does date from about 1150, the sources and affiliations of its style reside not in the workshop of the west facade but in a new group of emerging Gothic monuments.

Charles T. Little

Associate Curator
Department of Medieval Art
The Metropolitan Museum of Art

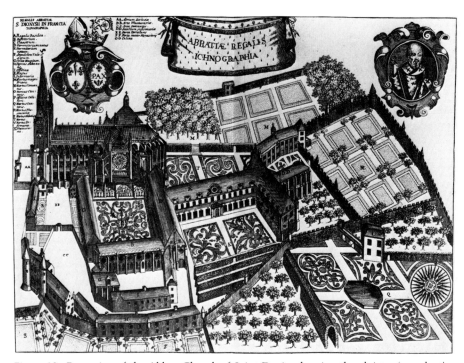

Figure 12. Engraving of the Abbey Church of Saint-Denis, showing the cloister (now lost). Seventeenth century. After Dom Michel Germain

Notes

1. *De Administratione*, XXVII, ed. Panofsky, 1979, 46–49.
2. Mâle, 1978, 177–83.
3. Crosby, 1969, 45–46; Gerson, 1970, 76–84.
4. Ross, 1940, 91–107; Pressouyre, 1976, 151–60.
5. Thérel, 1963, 156–58.
6. Von Simson, 1956, 141; Katzenellenbogen, 1959, 27–36; Thérel, 1963, 158. The harmony between kingship (*regnum*) and priesthood (*sacerdotium*) is emphasized by Suger himself in a letter of 1149 to the Archbishop of Rheims. Quoted in Katzenellenbogen, 1959, 33.
7. The column figures may reflect Christ's words, "Many prophets and kings have desired to see these things which ye see..." (Luke 10:24). See also Gerson, 1970, 140–61.
8. Pressouyre, 1970, 100.
9. Zarnecki, 1979, XV, 18.
10. Crosby and Blum, 1973, *passim*. A monograph on the twelfth-century sculptural program of the west facade and crypt, by Pamela Z. Blum, is now in preparation.
11. Montfaucon, 1729, I, pl. X.
12. Ostoia, 1955, 298–304.
13. The cloister is briefly described by Jacques Doublet, 1625, 325.
14. Bibliothèque Séguier, Nîmes, ms. 98.
15. Quarré, 1962, 283.
16. Porter, 1923, IV, 492.
17. Scher, 1969, nos. 34–36.
18. Pressouyre, 1973, figs. 12–15.
19. Lille, 1978, no. 23, illus.; Blum, 1978, 23–28.
20. Vöge, 1894, 198; Kerber, 1966, 45–46; Sauerländer, 1972, 44, 382.
21. Plancher, 1739, I, 521; Quarré, 1957; Schlink, 1970, 126–30.
22. For the reasoning of a date c. 1155–60 for Saint-Bénigne see Sauerländer, 1970, 36–38; Pressouyre, 1970, 19–25.
23. Kerber, 1966, pl. 3.

1. Heads, from the Central Portal

Limestone
About 1137–40

A. Double Heads of Apostles, from the Tympanum

Height, left, 18 cm. (7 1/16 in.), right, 14.5 cm. (5 11/16 in.); width, 16 cm. (6 5/16 in.)
Paris, Musée du Louvre, Inv. RF 54

B. Head of a Patriarch, from the Second Archivolt

Height, 25 cm. (9 7/8 in.)
Paris, Musée du Louvre, Inv. RF 52

Today, Suger's portal is a sad reflection of its original splendor. The ill effects of time, pollution, and repeated and extensive damage have been compounded by deplorable repairs, recutting, and unskillful restoration (Crosby, 1942, 6–11). In 1771, the portals were deliberately disfigured by the removal of all the column statues, the trumeau, and nearly all of the heads of the figures on the doorposts, tympanum, and archivolts (see fig. 9). Between 1813 and 1846, François Debret was charged with restoring the facade sculpture to its original state, but his ruthless and inept recarving incited such criticism that he was replaced in 1846 by Viollet-le-Duc, who completed the work on the abbey.

A careful appraisal by Sumner Crosby and Pamela Blum (1973) of all restorations on the central portal has led to a better understanding of what part of the iconographic program and which figure style is original to the twelfth century. In addition, the exact positions of the isolated heads now in the Louvre have been determined. In dimension and orientation the fragment with two apostles' heads corresponds to the group at the extreme left of the tympanum, which shows one apostle seated and another immediately behind (Crosby and Blum, 1973, 223–24). Although the heads are carved in the round, they are unfinished on the back and the sides since they would originally have been viewed only from the front and from below. In spite of their damaged condition, these bearded faces do not possess the surface modeling and interest in detail evident in the column figures. Furthermore, the sympathetic expression revealed in the large eyes with heavy lids displays a sense of life not previously encountered in portal sculpture. The heads of the apostles unveil a new image of man that is more natural than ideal, reflecting a significant shift in the mode of representation that is indicative of the Early Gothic style.

The head of a patriarch can also be linked to its original location on the portal. It comes from the first seated figure, holding a vial and a harp, on the right side of the second archivolt (Crosby and Blum, 1973, 254, pl. XX). In method of carving, this figure, which is in a fine state of preservation, is very similar to the apostles. However, the sculptor responsible for the head was different from the one who carved the apostles, and in the conception of the face, especially notable in the protrusion of the eyeballs and in the swelling of the surfaces, the style appears to be closer to some of the column figures (cat. no. 3). Thus, the sculptors of the central portal made an effort to harmonize their forms within the context of a new order and clarity of composition that completely subdued the imposing animation found on Romanesque portals.

Bibliography: Aubert and Beaulieu, 1950, 57; Crosby, 1970; Gerson, 1970, 18–55, 112–35; Sauerländer, 1972, 379–81; Crosby and Blum, 1973.

1B

2. Colonnettes, from the Doorjambs of the Lateral Portals of the West Facade

Limestone
About 1137–40

A. Colonnette
Height, 148.5 cm. (58½ in.), including 16 cm. (6⅝ in.) section of restoration; diameter, 13.5 cm. (5⅝ in.)
Paris, Musée du Louvre, Inv. RF 452/453

B. Colonnette
Height, 149.3 cm. (58¾ in.); diameter, 13.3 cm. (5¼ in.)
Paris, Musée de Cluny, CL 19576

C. Fragment of a Colonnette
Height, 34.1 cm. (13⁷⁄₁₆ in.); diameter, 13.2 cm. (5³⁄₁₆ in.)
Saint-Denis, Musée d'Art et d'Histoire

The decorative embellishment of the portals at Saint-Denis consisted not only of a richly sculpted iconographic program but also of foliate capitals, colonnettes, and friezes. These colonnettes are among the best-preserved elements to survive from the west facade. Their exceptional delicacy and crispness of carving demonstrate the high level of technical competency of the Saint-Denis atelier.

The two complete shafts are entirely filled with decoration, which consists of two spiral bands separated by narrow borders of embossed patterns. Within the bands of one colonnette (B) is a continuous vine scroll inhabited by putti and, as on the fragment (C), there are also birds, dogs, and fantastic beasts. The bands of the other shaft (A) consist only of pure floral ornament. The colonnette fragment (C) also has an inhabited vine scroll but here a nude figure armed with a lance and shield struggles against an attacking beast as affronted birds fall behind him. In all three examples, the sharpness of the undercutting greatly enhances the rhythmic flow of the entire design up the column.

The two complete colonnettes were used as models for the nineteenth-century restoration of the colonnettes in the doorjambs of the central portal. However, they originally came not from this portal but from the right sides of each of the two lateral portals (Crosby and Blum, 1973, 249–51). The scene on the fragment corresponds to descriptions and drawings of a colonnette made before the French Revolution; this colonnette probably came from the central portal (Le Gentil de la Galasière, 1791, 390–438, pls. XVII, XVIII).

All of these colonnettes are by one sculptor, who was one of the most original working on the facade. This preference for completely patterned shafts reappears in the same form at Chartres, on other Early Gothic portals, and on the Apostles Relief (cat. no. 6). The classical manner of the nude figures in these inhabited scrolls apparently had widespread appeal. The same motifs recur on the portals at Lincoln Cathedral, which probably date from before 1146 (Zarnecki, 1979, XV, 17, pls. 29–31). However, they

2A

2B

37

are also found in contemporary metalwork, manuscript illumination, and ivory carving, and may reflect a natural delight in lively decorative forms. At Saint-Denis the cross-fertilization of the different workshops occasionally produced similar decorative patterns. Thus, it is not surprising to find acanthus patterns comparable to those on the colonnettes in the borders of the ambulatory windows (cat. nos. 15, 18), both artists perhaps utilizing a common model for their designs.

Bibliography: Le Gentil de la Galasière, 1791, 390–438; Stoddard, 1952, 4–6; Crosby and Blum, 1973, 249–51; Zarnecki, 1979, IV, 152–58, XV, 1–24.

2C

2B (detail)

3. Four Heads, from the Jamb Sculptures on the West Facade

Limestone
About 1137–40

A. Head of a Queen, from the Central Portal
Height, 37 cm. (14 9/16 in.); width, 20 cm. (7 7/8 in.)
Paris, Collection Jean Osouf

B. Head of a King, from the Central Portal
Height, 35 cm. (13 3/4 in.); width at crown, 20 cm. (7 7/8 in.)
Baltimore, Walters Art Gallery, 27.22

C. Head of a King, from the Left Portal
Height, 36 cm. (14 3/16 in.); width at crown, 21.5 cm. (8 1/2 in.)
Baltimore, Walters Art Gallery, 27.21

D. Head of a King, from the Left Portal
Height, 36 cm. (14 3/16 in.); width, 21 cm. (8 1/4 in.)
Cambridge, Fogg Art Museum, Harvard University, 1920.30

These four surviving royal heads were originally from the central and left portals of Saint-Denis. Identification of them is based upon Antoine Benoist's drawings (figs. 13–16), made for Montfaucon's engravings (fig. 11). Only the head of the queen has escaped severe damage and restoration. Its excellent condition is revealed not only in the sharpness of the carving but also in the deeply drilled pupil of the left eye, which still retains its original lead. Identified by Léon Pressouyre (1976), this queen's head with a crown of large oval cabochons and long braids with crisscrossed ribbons is identical to Benoist's drawing (fig. 13). Because this type of queen with long braids reappears on numerous Early Gothic facades where she can occasionally be identified as the Queen of Sheba, this head from the central portal may also represent the celebrated Old Testament queen (Gerson, 1970, 153–58). The splendid head is stylistically and technically very similar to the head of a king from the same portal, which has undergone extensive and disfiguring restoration (now removed). Both heads initially give the impression, especially from the front, of rigid geometric shapes with sharply carved eyes, hair, and crown. But when carefully observed, particularly from below, as they were intended to be viewed, a delicate modeling of the planes is also revealed. The emphatic strengthening of the eyes by means of simplification and the bold-

ness of detail heighten rather than diminish the monumental effect of these noble heads. Originally the heads were semidetached from the shafts, as indicated by their partially finished backs, and were looking slightly downward.

In contrast, the heads from the left portal (C, D) are by another sculptor and convey a different impression. Here the modeling is generally softer but the integration of parts is somewhat inorganically achieved, such as in the highly stylized hair and the protruding upper lip. The Saint-Denis provenance of the Fogg head has been unjustly questioned because of several factors: it is said to come from Poitou, its shape is more tapered than the others, and the pupils are not characteristically drilled (Cahn and Seidel, 1979, 184–85). Yet the crown type consisting of feather motifs is unique to Saint-Denis, as reflected in the Montfaucon engravings, and one can find at Chartres column figures with both drilled and undrilled pupils. These two heads from the lateral portal share the same heavy ears, rhythmic treatment of the hair, and modeling of the cheeks.

With the knowledge of these four heads from the facade, we are in a better position to understand the artistic sources and influences of the Saint-Denis facade sculptures. Wilhelm Vöge (1894, 80–90), knowing only the drawings and engravings of Montfaucon, propounded the theory that the Saint-Denis figures were the work of an atelier from either Saint-Étienne in Toulouse, or Moissac. With few exceptions (Aubert, 1945, 243–48), this theory has prevailed until recently. The bold morphology of the faces and idiomatic treatment of the eyes, especially those of the queen, seem to have evolved from contemporary sculptural tendencies within the Île-de-France. Pressouyre (1976, 156) recognized the same style in the capitals from Saint-Étienne at Dreux (now destroyed), where the heads possess a similar elementary force. Therefore, the mutations of style evident in these royal heads are more the direct result of indigenous styles characteristic of the Île-de-France region—reacting with the possible influence of metalwork—than of the transplantation of a style from southwestern France. In fact, they evoke a new expression of profound solemnity that clearly marks the decisive changes that led to the Early Gothic style.

Bibliography: Montfaucon, 1729, I, 193; Ross, 1940, 91–109; Wixom, 1967, III-14; Scher, 1969, cat. nos. 52–53; Pressouyre, 1976, 151–60; Cahn and Seidel, 1979, 184–85; Panofsky, 1979, 166–67.

Figure 13. Drawing by Antoine Benoist of a lost jamb figure of a queen, from the central portal. Seventeenth century. Paris, Bibliothèque Nationale

3A

B

Figure 14. Drawing by Antoine Benoist
of a lost jamb figure of a
king, from the central
portal. Seventeenth century.
Paris, Bibliothèque
Nationale

41

Figure 15. Drawing by Antoine Benoist
of a lost jamb figure of a
king, from the left portal.
Seventeenth century. Paris,
Bibliothèque Nationale

3C

42

Figure 16. Drawing by Antoine Benoist of a lost jamb figure of a king, from the left portal. Seventeenth century. Paris, Bibliothèque Nationale

4 (detail)

4. Column Figure of a Nimbed King, from the Old Cloister

Limestone
About 1150
Height, 115 cm. (45¼ in.); diameter of column, 13.5 cm. (5 5/16 in.); maximum width, 20 cm. (7 7/8 in.)
New York, The Metropolitan Museum of Art, Joseph Pulitzer Bequest, 1920, 20.157

According to Montfaucon, this column statue was in the oldest part of the cloister and is the only complete statue known to have survived, of all the architectural decoration executed during the abbacy of Suger. Because of the method of execution—cutting diagonally into a squared length of stone—the statue is attached along its entire axis to the column, producing two basic cylindrical units, the statue and the colonnette. This diagonal approach forces the immobile figure into a compressed area so that the arms and scroll, now broken, are subjected to the initial shape of the block. Unlike the faces of the column statues of the west facade, the face on this column is in a strictly frontal position, adhering closely to the shaft and having no eye contact with the viewer.

This nimbed figure can be identified as a king since he wears a crown that is mounted with large jewels set alternately in vertical and horizontal positions; those set vertically project above the rim. Between each large jewel are smaller settings, with rims consisting of pearled borders. This type of crown and its settings are similar to those of the queen (cat. no. 3A) from the west facade. The king wears a long-sleeved waist-length tunic (or *chainse*) that is slit at the neck, under which a full-length skirt of pleated fabric falls in long parallel folds. A rich girdle, from which long tassels hang down, holds the tunic in place. Oddly, however, the tassels are not connected to the girdle but seem to be attached somehow under the tunic. This apparently disconcerting arrangement would originally have appeared quite normal because the hands holding an open scroll, now broken, would have concealed this area. The dress of the figure is unusual for a king (Vöge, 1894, 199), but not entirely unique—a point that deserves some comment since the authenticity of the figure has been challenged, in part, on these grounds. Similar neck openings occur on the costumes of figures in the cloister at Arles (Stoddard, 1973, fig. 361) and on those of the apostles on the facade of Saint-Gilles-du-Gard (Stoddard, 1973, figs. 26, 33, 77). A number of twelfth-century Old Testament kings appear with girdles, especially within the context of the Tree of Jesse, such as in the Saint-Denis window (Grodecki, 1976, figs. 36, 49) and the west window at Chartres (Grodecki, 1977, pl. 86). A figure of Peter(?) on a northern French Early Gothic multifigured column (The Glencairn Museum, Academy of the New Church, Bryn Athyn, Pennsylvania) appears to wear a similar costume with a tasseled girdle. Thus, this Old Testament king and

4

the other figures in the cloister recorded by Montfaucon must bear the same significance as those statues originally on the west facade: the royal genealogy of Christ.

An assessment of the style of the cloister king is partly restricted by its present condition. The figure has undergone some redefinition of detail, resulting in a somewhat sterile effect for some passages. This is particularly noticeable in the overly emphatic grooving of the hair, beard, and decorative hem patterns. Without considering the question of recarving, the figure often has been thought to be a nineteenth-century work (Pressouyre, 1967, 249, n. 1, 1976, 158, n. 19; Sauerländer, 1970, 37, 1972, 44, 382). Despite the problem of condition, a number of parallels—especially in details—can be made to other Saint-Denis sculptures. From the cloister itself, the capitals with human heads now in the Musée d'Art et d'Histoire at Saint-Denis (cat. no. 5A) and in the Musée des Antiquités in Rouen (fig. 18) bear striking resemblances to the facial type of the king, particularly in the long hair curled at the neck, and the shape and cutting of the eyes. The tendency toward richly detailed garments with a range of decorative hem patterns finds a close parallel in the Apostles Relief (cat. no. 6).

Ex collections: Marquis de Migieu (Savigny-les-Beaune); Vicomte de Vaulchier; Alphonse Kann (Paris).

Bibliography: Doublet, 1625, 325; Montfaucon, 1729, I, 57–58; Plancher, 1739, I, 521–22; Vöge, 1894, 197–200; Breck, 1921, XVI, March, 48–52; Van Marle, 1921, X, December, no. 1; Ostoia, 1955, June, 298–304; Quarré, 1957, 193, 194, 1962, 283; Grodecki, 1959, vol. 117, part 4, 273, 276; Formigé, 1960, 19; Kerber, 1966, 44–46; Pressouyre, 1967, 249, 1976, XV/1, 158, n. 19; Wixom, 1967, no. 3, 14; Paris, 1968, no. 1; Sauerländer, 1970, 44, 382; Schlink, 1970, 126–30; Crosby, 1970, 10, 11 n. 13, 1972, 67; Panofsky, 1979, 167.

Figure 17. Drawing by Antoine Benoist of a column statue of a king, from the old cloister. Seventeenth century. Paris, Bibliothèque Nationale

5. Capitals, from the Old Cloister
Limestone
1150

A. Double Capital with Human Heads
Height, 26.2 cm. (10 5/16 in.); length at top, 37 cm.
(14 9/16 in.); diameter, 29.5 cm. (11 5/8 in.); inside
diameter of socket, 13.5 cm. (5 5/16 in.)
Saint-Denis, Musée d'Art et d'Histoire

B. Capital with Harpies
Height, 19.3 cm. (7 5/8 in.); length, 25.5 cm. (10 1/16
in.); diameter, 29.5 cm. (11 5/8 in.)
Paris, Musée du Louvre, Inv. RF 525

A group of capitals, both double and single, are re-
puted to have come from the cloister at Saint-Denis.
Several have a nineteenth-century provenance, but
at that time the abbey was a central collecting point
for sculptural decoration of the region. Thus, it is
only from direct internal evidence, such as size,
style, and technique, that a cloister source may be
postulated for these two capitals. Both are carved in
the round, with each face containing a central palmette and either a human head (A) or a harpy (B)
emerging from the corners. With their wings spread,
the harpies placed on the corners of the single capital
dominate the surface. A more complete capital of
this type, similar in dimensions and style—and probably also from the cloister—is in the Musée des Antiquités in Rouen (fig. 18). A number of points of
comparison can be made between these capitals with
human heads or harpies and the column statue of
an Old Testament king (cat. no. 4). The size of the
capital is proportionately correct for the height of
the column figure, and the diameter of the shaft
attached to the column figure is identical to the inside diameter of the partly broken socket at the base
of the capital into which the shaft could have fit.
Furthermore, there is a close resemblance between
the bearded face on the capital and that of the king,
especially in their shape and in the cutting of the
eyes.

Other capitals of similar dimension and style may
also be assigned to the Saint-Denis cloister: two double capitals in the Musée de Cluny (Inv. 18925 A,B)—
one with pairs of winged beasts holding a man's head
and a lion's head, the other with fantastic beasts
(Sauerländer, 1962, 100, fig. 6); a double-foliate capital in the Louvre (Inv. RF 496–497; Aubert and
Beaulieu, 1950, nos. 64–65); and another harpy capital in the Maison de la Légion d'Honneur at Saint-
Denis (Pressouyre, 1970, 20). As a group, these capitals represent a type that appears throughout much
of northern France from about 1140 to 1170. Both
the west facade and the exterior of the choir of Saint-
Denis display capitals with fantastic beasts (Wulf,
1979, pls. 19, 22, 43). The specific style of the capitals developed in the Saint-Denis cloister appears
to have influenced a number of Early Gothic monuments. Within the immediate vicinity of Saint-
Denis, some of the capitals in the choir of Saint-
Germain-des-Prés reveal a striking similarity, suggesting that the same workshop was responsible for
both churches. Likewise, in the choir of Notre-Dame
the same type occurs (Wulf, 1979, pl. 128). Equally
significant is the portal decoration of Notre-Dame-
en-Vaux at Châlons-sur-Marne, dating from after
1157, which has its distinct sources in the Saint-
Denis cloister capitals (Sauerländer, 1962; Pressouyre, 1970).

Figure 18. Capital with harpies, from the old cloister. c. 1150.
Rouen, Musée des Antiquités

Bibliography: (A) unpublished; (B) Aubert and Beaulieu,
    1950, no. 62; Pressouyre, 1970, 20; Brouillette, 1977,
    no. 28.

5A (detail)

5A

49

5B

6. Bas-Relief with the Twelve Apostles

Limestone
About 1150–51
Height, 52.5 cm. (20 11/16 in.); length, 205.3 cm. (80 13/16 in.); depth, 10.3 cm. (4 1/16 in.)
Cathedral of Saint-Denis, Chapel of Saint Osmana

This extraordinary relief was found in 1947 by Sumner Crosby during the course of excavations in the south transept of the abbey. The momentous discovery has greatly enriched our understanding of Early Gothic art. Because the relief had been placed upside down, to serve as the lid of a thirteenth-century plaster sarcophagus, it survived in pristine condition. The decorative details that fill nearly the entire surface are as fresh and as crisp today as when they were first carved.

Disposed within a continuous arcade are the twelve apostles; each, except one, is identified by an inscription carved on his book or scroll or nearby on the architecture. Only the centrally placed Saint Peter is without an inscription but he holds an enormous pair of keys, his symbol. Though each apostle is enclosed in an arch, they are arranged in pairs, with varying poses and gestures, as if engaged in dialogue. The idea of conversing *in disputatione* emphasizes the Early Christian theme of the apostles as teachers of Christian dogma (Crosby, 1972, 63–64). This theme became increasingly popular in the twelfth century and was utilized during the time of Suger in two other Saint-Denis works: in the apostles flanking Christ as Judge on the central tympanum of the west facade and in the ivory panels from the portable altar (cat. no. 28A,B), which, iconographically, are similar to the relief.

The bas-relief was never intended to cover a coffin, but its true function continues to be a puzzle. Discarded from some unfulfilled project, the relief

is actually unfinished. Some of the garments of the apostles lack ornamental borders and some of the pupils of the eyes are not drilled. The most significant clue to its unfinished state appears at the right end of the relief, which contains a palmette design only partially incised, clearly illustrating the working method of the sculptor. The ends were, therefore, intended to be exposed, and this physical evidence indicates that they would have abutted another piece at right angles, since the continuous decoration stops abruptly. Rejecting the reconstruction by Jules Formigé as an altar retable, Crosby (1972, 15–24) has hypothesized that the bas-relief was destined for a basilica-like tabernacle-altar (now lost) to contain relics of the three patron saints, Denis, Rusticus, and Eleutherius (see page 101). He maintains that the shrine, or reliquary sarcophagus, of Saint Denis was begun in stone, and that the bas-relief was to have decorated its right side. Before completion, Suger received a "wealth of gold," which induced him to create an even more resplendent tabernacle in precious metal, but it too is now lost (*De Administratione*, XXXI, ed. Panofsky, 1979, 54–57; *De Consecratione*, V, ed. Panofsky, 1979, 104–7). Thus, if Suger's elliptical allusion to a change of plan is correct, the bas-relief went unfinished and unused until the thirteenth century, when it was placed on the coffin of an unidentified person. Nevertheless, the relief is thematically complete in itself and does not require a larger context in which to be understood.

A more likely function is that it served as the side of a wall tomb (Sauerländer, 1974, 438), which would also have permitted the decoration on the ends to continue on another slab but would still have left open the unanswered question of the unfinished edge. In support of this theory is a bas-relief similar in iconography, composition, and dimensions, on the tomb of Abbot Pierre de Saine-Fontaine (d. 1110) at Airvault (Deux Sèvres) (Crosby, 1972, pl. 81). Tomb reliefs of the twelve apostles existed throughout Early Christian Gaul, and it is not impossible that the Saint-Denis relief is an intentional revival of that earlier practice. Others sporadically occur, such as on the tomb of Henry VII at Pisa (Bauch, 1976, figs. 272, 274). If the bas-relief were intended for a tomb, it must have been commissioned by a major patron, judging from the exceptional quality of the carving.

When Suger died on January 13, 1151, his "body was solemnly committed to the ground" in the presence of King Louis VII and a distinguished gathering of bishops, abbots, knights, and monks. Given Suger's obsession with his own posterity—at least four representations of him and at least thirteen inscriptions referring to him by name were strategically placed within the abbey—a tomb with the twelve apostles, symbolizing the corporate body of the Christian Church, would be exactly what one would expect for his final resting place. Between the time of his last illness in the fall of 1150 and his death the tomb could have been nearly completed, but in the rush to have it ready for the funeral some

51

6 (detail)

52

minor areas may have been left unfinished. In 1259, the tomb was moved to the south transept and completely renovated, thus relegating the bas-relief to oblivion until its discovery in 1947.

The artistic origins and training of the sculptor of the bas-relief are revealed in his predilection for rendering delicate and profuse decorative patterns that dominate the entire surface, producing a *horror vacui* effect. Indeed, this bewildering array of eighty different patterns is a virtual compendium of twelfth-century ornament, and no other single object of the High Middle Ages can compare to it. Without question, the relief betrays the technique, vocabulary, and forms of goldsmiths' work (Crosby, 1972, 56–72). This connection and dependence is evident in even the smallest details, such as some of the columns standing on minute twisted and arcaded bases with simulated filigree and granulation. In addition, many of the decorative motifs on the bas-relief can be found on sculpture from the west facade, on stained-glass borders, and on treasury objects (cat. nos. 2 A–C, 15, 28A,B), reinforcing the idea of an active interrelationship among the artists employed by Suger.

The apostles, with their compact proportions, create a tension of scale within the architectural frame. Yet the rhythmic ordering of the poses, gestures, and of the arrangement of drapery patterns conceals this tension and is one of the main characteristics of the Saint-Denis style. The source of this style and of some of the patterns can possibly be found in Lotharingian metalwork, since Suger states that goldsmiths from Lorraine executed the pedestal and the Great Cross for the new chevet (Crosby, 1970, 8–9, 1972, *passim*; Wixom, page 101). At the same time, however, there are many important affinities shared by this relief, the apostles on the lintel of the facade at Chartres, and the Last Supper tympanum at Saint-Bénigne in Dijon. By extension, the likelihood that the Apostles Relief was destined for the tomb of Abbot Suger tends to support a date of about 1150.

Bibliography: Crosby, 1947, 167–81, 1950, 253, 1953, 55, 1966, 25–26, 1970, 8–9, 1972, *passim*; Stoddard, 1952, 60; Quarré, 1957, 193; Formigé, 1960, 131–34; Kerber, 1966, 46; Sauerländer, 1972, 387–88, 1974, 438–39.

7. Foliate Capital

Limestone
About 1140–50
Height, 30 cm. (11¹³⁄₁₆ in.); depth at top, 32 cm. (12⅝ in.); length at top, 45 cm. (17¾ in.); diameter at base, 36 cm. (14³⁄₁₆ in.)
Saint-Denis, Musée Lapidaire

A rich acanthus leaf pattern is symmetrically arranged around the surface of the capital. This type of decoration appears throughout Saint-Denis; particularly close in style are some of the capitals in the choir (Wulf, 1979, fig. 58). As an endless variation on a motif—compare this capital with cat. no. 8—such acanthus patterns were employed not only as an integral part of the architecture and sculpture of the abbey, but also on stained glass and precious objects.

A number of miscellaneous capitals and architectural fragments have been found at the abbey. However, the exact location from which this capital came—if ever it was installed—is not known.

Bibliography: unpublished.

7

8. Impost Blocks with Acanthus Decoration

Limestone
About 1144–50

A. Height, 38.6 cm. (15³⁄₁₆ in.); width, 67.9 cm. (26¾ in.); depth, 41.3 cm. (16¼ in.)
Bryn Athyn, Pennsylvania, The Glencairn Museum, Academy of the New Church

B. Height, 39.8 cm. (15¹¹⁄₁₆ in.); width, 82.5 cm. (32½ in.); depth, 49.5 cm. (19½ in.)
Bryn Athyn, Pennsylvania, The Glencairn Museum, Academy of the New Church

C. Height, 36.8 cm. (14½ in.); width, 81.2 cm. (32 in.); depth, 34.3 cm. (13½ in.)
Bryn Athyn, Pennsylvania, The Glencairn Museum, Academy of the New Church

D. Height, 51.5 cm. (20¼ in.); width, 63.5 cm. (25 in.); depth, 39.1 cm. (15⅜ in.)
New York, The Metropolitan Museum of Art, Rogers Fund, 1913, 13.152.1

8D (detail)

Although these impost blocks are all of different dimension, they share the same type of decoration, carving technique, and weathering. Three sides of each of the blocks are ornamented with an organic frieze of repeated pairs of acanthus leaves enveloping an axial pinecone. Only one of them (D) is more refined in its carving and contains pairs of symmetrically placed birds that peck at the pinecones.

A Saint-Denis provenance for these impost blocks cannot be documented although one (D) is said to come from the abbey. Analogous types of decoration can be found on the impost blocks of the piers in the ambulatory of the crypt built by Suger (Crosby, 1972, fig. 58). However, as noted by Cahn (1977, 74), it is only in this area of the church that comparative types of acanthus decoration are located. This suggests a date some time after 1144 for the blocks. It is not unlikely that such impost blocks were prepared *en masse* in the workshop for eventual use, but these four may never have actually been installed. Crosby has suggested that they might have been intended for use in Suger's replacement of the old Carolingian nave or transept, which was not constructed until the thirteenth century (Crosby, 1953, 48). However, because of their varying dimensions, their exact function and context remain an open question.

Bibliography: Breck, 1913, 249–50; Cahn, 1977.

8A

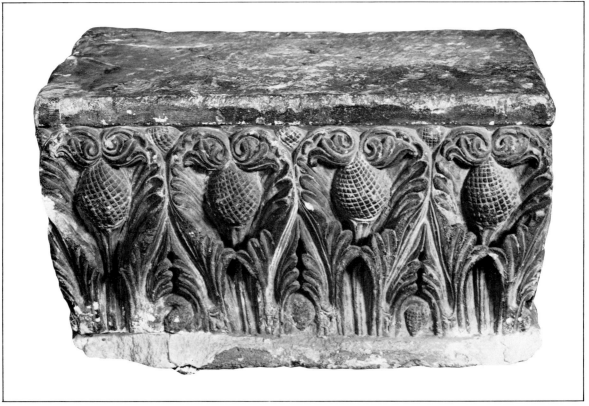

56

8B

8C

57

8D

9. Abacus Fragments
Limestone
About 1150

A. Height, 16.2 cm. (6⅜ in.); length, 27 cm. (10⅝ in.)
Paris, Musée du Louvre, Inv. RF 510

B. Height, 10.6 cm. (4³⁄₁₆ in.); length, 21.6 cm. (8½ in.)
Baltimore, Walters Art Gallery, 27.498

9A

Although both of these fragments from an abacus have a Saint-Denis provenance, no complete example exists at the abbey. The more intact fragment shows a bearded head enframed by a palmette and a pinecone motif not unlike those on the impost blocks from Saint-Denis (cat. no. 8). In spite of the fragmentary state of the abacus, the carving is remarkably crisp. The stylization of the face finds striking parallels in the Apostles Relief (cat. no. 6), and a similar type of mask within the palmette on the abacus fragment also occurs on the relief's unfinished end (Crosby, 1972, figs. 50, 51). This type of bearded mask begins to appear in sculpture from the Île-de-France from about 1150, first at Chartres and in the cloister capitals at Saint-Denis. In fact, the face can be stylistically related to the face on the double capital with winged beasts holding a man's head, in the Musée de Cluny (Inv. 18925 A), suggesting that these abacus fragments once were part of the decoration of the cloister.

Bibliography: Ross, 1940, 104, fig. 20; Aubert and Beaulieu, 1950, 59, no. 58; Brouillette, 1977, no. 27.

9B

Stained Glass at Saint-Denis

In spite of the remarkably careful restoration of the choir of Saint-Denis conducted by Viollet-le-Duc beginning in 1847, the windows there now are no more like those installed by Suger than is the present sculptural program like the one that he originally devised for the west facade (fig. 6). It is ironic that those windows, having survived both the pillage of the abbey by the Huguenots and the French Revolution, were all but destroyed in order to be exhibited in a museum. Of the estimated 140 panels of stained glass removed from the disaffected abbey church by Alexandre Lenoir in 1799 to his Musée des Monuments Français in Paris, only thirty-one were ever replaced in the choir.[1] The rest were either smashed in transit by oxcart to Paris or sold by Lenoir himself to private collectors abroad. Many of the pieces now in museums are those that were dispersed in Lenoir's time or later.

The most important documents that guided Viollet-le-Duc's restoration of the windows in the abbey were the drawings of the architect Charles Percier, who was commissioned in the winter of 1794–95 to design a reinstallation of several royal tombs.[2] While at Saint-Denis, Percier sketched some of Suger's windows, the only record of their original appearance that is known. Percier's rapidly executed sketch (fig. 19), difficult to interpret, resulted in certain mistakes on the part of Viollet-le-Duc and his glaziers Henri and Alfred Gérente that have since been rectified in the studies of Louis Grodecki.[3] That Lenoir was primarily interested in narrative rather than ornamental panels for his museum, and that a number of borders from Suger's windows and scenes unsuitable for exhibition were stored at Saint-Denis, provided additional information for the restoration. Some of the borders of these original pieces (figs. 20a–c) were traced by the young architect Just Lisch in 1849, perhaps to serve as models for the restoration.[4] The original panels were not, however, reemployed in the windows but, instead, were returned to the storage depot at Saint-Denis and gradually disappeared, only to reappear on the art market half a century later. The Lisch tracings have since permitted further identification of lost pieces. Viollet-le-Duc also used Suger's own descriptions of his windows in creating new scenes for sections that were lost (fig. 21).

Suger described only three of his windows in his treatise *De Administratione*, but he also implied that both the upper choir and the crypt were filled with stained glass.[5] The first window, which he said began the series, "in the chevet of the church," was the Tree of Jesse window.

Figure 19. Drawing by Charles Percier of some of Suger's windows. 1794–95. Compiègne, Bibliothèque de la Ville

Much has been written about this, the best preserved of Suger's windows.[6] Except for the panel that depicted the sleeping Jesse—shown in Percier's drawing—the entire central portion with the royal ancestors and the Virgin and Christ seated upon the branches of the tree, still survives (fig. 22). A number of the prophets that flank the tree are still in the window, and others have been discovered elsewhere. Even the palmette border, which copies the original design, contains old fragments. Suger described two additional windows in greater detail, even mentioning the scenes that were included. Both of these, a Life of Moses and what Panofsky has called an "Anagogical window," still exist in part (figs. 23–24).[7] These descriptions plus remains of the glass at Saint-Denis and pieces discovered in collections both in Europe and the United States have permitted Louis Grodecki to reconstruct the iconography and the symbolic meaning of the glazing program of the choir.[8]

Pervading Suger's writings and physically manifested in the luminosity of the new windows was the philosophy of Pseudo-Dionysius the Areopagite.[9] This obscure figure, probably the author of the sixth-century *De Coelesti Hierarchia*, in which he established light as the primary source of faith and inspiration, had special significance for the abbey. Pseudo-Dionysius the Areopagite had been identified by the monks of Saint-Denis with Dionysius the Aeropagite, mentioned in Acts 17:34 as a follower of Saint Paul. He had further been identified with Saint Denis, the martyred first Bishop of Paris, whose burial place became the site of the abbey and who is its patron saint. Given the prevailing belief that there was a direct historical connection between Saint Denis and the Apostle Paul, it is not surprising that both the Epistles of Paul and the Neoplatonic philosophy of Pseudo-Dionysius inspired the iconographic program devised for the choir windows. Still another factor implicit in the program was the relationship that existed between the abbey and the French kings.[10] As the burial place of the monarchy, keeper of the royal crowns and of the Banner of Saint Denis (see pages 103–4), the abbey enjoyed special political privileges that were symbolically recorded in the windows of the choir.

The windows of the central chapel, dedicated to the Virgin, represented the Tree of Jesse and the Infancy of Christ, portions of which are still *in situ* (figs. 22, 25). The iconographic theme in this chapel was the Incarnation, with its revelation in the Old Testament by Isaiah and its manifestation in the New Testament through the Gospels. To the left, in the chapel of Saint Peregrinus, were the Life of Moses window and the Anagogical window, defined by Grodecki as allegories from the Epistles of Saint Paul on the relationship between the Old and New Testaments (figs. 23, 24).[11] Large sections of these windows still exist but the glazing of the chapel dedicated to Saint Cucuphas, on the opposite side, is conjectural. Grodecki has proposed, based on the Percier drawing and on one remaining panel, that scenes from Christ's Passion were opposed with Old Testament prefigurations of these events.[12] The one remaining panel is the scene of the marking of the Tau sign on the foreheads of the Jews, a common Old Testament type for the Crucifixion (fig. 26). The major theme for the iconographic program of Suger's windows in the choir of Saint-Denis was, therefore, an interpretation of relationships existing between Mosaic and Christian law as both are revealed and explained through the Incarnation. Much of this symbolism was derived from the philosophical writings and connections falsely attributed to the abbey's patron, Saint Denis, but additional links to biblical history in the form of relics of the Passion possessed by the abbey were equally fictitious. In an attempt to authenticate these relics, which were presented to the abbey by Charles the Bald in the ninth century, the monks had, at that

a

b

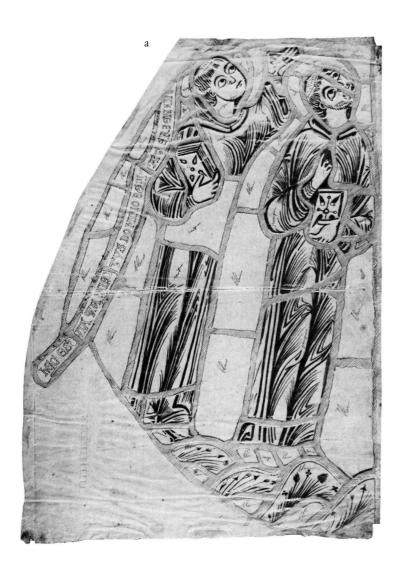

Figure 20 a, b, c. Tracings by Just Lisch of the two monks from the Saint Benedict window (cat. no. 17; now in the Musée de Cluny, Paris) and of two border sections (cat. nos. 18, 22; now in The Glencairn Museum, Academy of the New Church, Bryn Athyn, Pennsylvania). c. 1849. Paris, Archives des Monuments Historiques

time, fabricated an account of a voyage by Charlemagne to the Holy Land in which he had received these very relics from Constantine.[13] This historically impossible account and the story of the First Crusade were depicted in two additional windows of the choir (cat. nos. 20, 21). Added before Suger's death, perhaps on the occasion of Louis VII's departure for the Second Crusade in 1147, these windows magnified the role of the French monarchs as defenders of the faith and the abbey's own religious authority as the repository of these most-sacred relics. Well documented by drawings made before 1721 and by Percier's sketch, these windows have disappeared except for two panels now in the United States (fig. 27).

Suger evidently included windows of a purely decorative design in the choir. Known from Percier's drawings and from remains that still exist in the chapels, they were composed of repetitive motifs of griffins and foliage (fig. 28). Less expensive because of the inclusion of colorless glass and the repetitiveness of the design, these windows may have been considered only temporary until an increase in funds permitted the addition of narrative windows. The legends of at least two saints, one noted by Percier, were also included at Saint-Denis. A number of panels now scattered in various collections are scenes from the life of Saint Benedict and one panel is from the story of Saint Vincent of Saragossa (cat. nos. 17, 19).[14] These hagiographical subjects may have been placed in the crypt where Suger implied that there were also stained-glass windows. The chapel of Saint Benedict was the first on the north side in the new crypt, and, although there was no altar dedicated to Saint Vincent in the twelfth century, a relic of this popular saint reposed in the matutinal altar located at the entrance to the monks' stalls in the old part of the church.[15]

Little has been written on the style of the windows at Saint-Denis. Grodecki has postulated that a major atelier was responsible for most of the choir glazing with a second workshop, originating in the Meuse, having glazed the chapel in which the window depicting the Tau sign was placed. A third atelier created the Saint Benedict window.[16] Crosby has envisioned an international workshop in which artisans in the various crafts, working closely together for a short period of time, evolved a style that was indigenous to Saint-Denis.[17] The unimpeachable authority, Suger himself, said that his stained-glass windows were made by the "exquisite hands of many masters from different regions."[18] In fact, a number of different hands can be detected in the glass from Saint-Denis but, at the same time, there is an amazing homogeneity of style. The major problem in this stylistic study is that no windows from which comparisons may be drawn predate those at Saint-Denis. To compound the problem, French manuscript illumination from the first half of the twelfth century has been studied only in general terms.

Among the "masters" called to Saint-Denis by Suger, the painter and assistants who made the Tree of Jesse window may be identified. This "exquisite hand," creator of stylized yet elegantly flowing folds of drapery and lush, bejeweled ornament, may have come from Burgundy, where a similar style can be detected in manuscripts illuminated at the Abbey of Cîteaux. Far less elegant are the dwarf-like figures and profusely decorated furnishings in scenes attributable to the workshop that produced the Infancy of Christ window. This master seems to have been established over a period of time at Saint-Denis, for his hand can also be detected in the Saint Vincent panel and in the First Crusade and Charlemagne windows. Perhaps it was to him, as Suger stated, that the abbot entrusted the upkeep of his stained glass.[19] The style of this master is closest to the style of the west windows at Chartres of some ten years later, and also to that of the Apostles bas-relief at Saint-Denis (cat. no. 6). The earliest comparisons with this master's work are, however, the relief

c

65

Figure 21. Cartoon by Alfred Gérente for the Unveiling of Moses, designed after
Suger's description of the original window. 1852. Bryn Athyn,
Pennsylvania, The Glencairn Museum, Academy of the New Church

sculptures of the west facade. Had we a firmer grasp of manuscript illumination at Saint-Denis and at Chartres in the early twelfth century, perhaps a definite origin for the style of this workshop might be found.

A far more highly skilled painter executed the windows of Moses and the Allegories of Saint Paul. Carefully wrought details, such as the inscriptions that form a part of the designs, recall the filigree and granulation techniques employed in metalwork and suggest that this master had been trained as a goldsmith. Perhaps he was called to Saint-Denis by Suger as a glass painter, together with his metalsmiths from Lorraine. Unfortunately, the enameled objects that might prove this point are all later in date. The griffin windows, which may be the work of this master's assistants, also appear to be based on metalwork.

The technique of the Saint Benedict Master is mediocre by comparison. His elongated figures, whose draperies are characterized by parallel or diagonally placed folds, are stylistically unlike those of the previously discussed masters. Monotonously composed scenes and richly delineated ornament distinguish his work. Grodecki has compared this style to manuscripts from the Manche region of northwestern France,[20] but there are also comparisons to be drawn with the twelfth-century illuminations at Mont-Saint-Michel further west.

Even though examples of Mosan illumination are scarce and of a later date, they afford the best comparisons of style with the panel that depicts the marking of the Tau sign. The work of this master, a painter of consummate skill, is quite different from that of the others who made the windows for Suger's choir. In a certain sense, his well-proportioned figures anticipate that classical phase of Gothic art that makes its appearance at the end of the twelfth century.

Though the styles of Suger's masters are distinct, this distinction is one of degree rather than substance. There is, in the glazing of Saint-Denis, a homogeneity that would not again be reached in twelfth-century glass painting. Within the short space of three years the entire choir and crypt were constructed. In no more than a year most of the windows in the choir were presumably in place. Many glaziers must have been at work, probably in the same shed, near where the kilns were located. Journeymen and apprentices were undoubtedly exchanged by masters as the need arose. Designs and painting styles must have been adopted into a great international workshop that included all the "exquisite hands" working in stone and metal as well as in glass.

Jane Hayward
Curator
The Cloisters
The Metropolitan Museum of Art

Notes

1. See Grodecki, 1976, 42–46, for an extensive study of the glass, with documentation during its removal and exhibition by Lenoir.
2. Grodecki, 1976, 40.
3. Viollet-le-Duc's most serious error was in his reconstruction of the Infancy of Christ window, which he restored, like the Childhood of Christ window at Chartres, in horizontal registers of alternating round and square panels. He could not have known, because of the disappearance of many of the

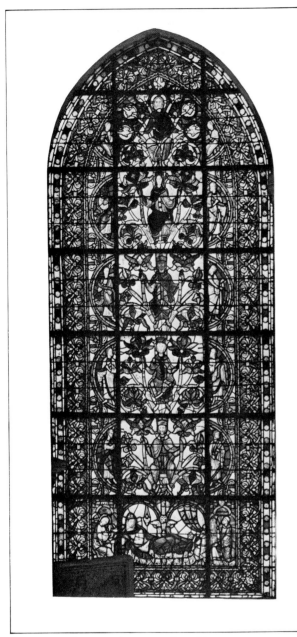

Figure 22. The Tree of Jesse window, Choir,
Chapel of the Virgin

Figure 23. The Moses window, Choir, Chapel of
Saint Peregrinus

Figure 24. The Anagogical window, or the Allegories of Saint
Paul, Choir, Chapel of Saint Peregrinus

Figure 25. The Infancy of Christ window, Choir,
Chapel of the Virgin

69

Figure 26. The Visions of Ezekiel window, with the Marking of the Tau Sign (center), Choir, Chapel of Saint Cucuphas

Figure 27. Engraving by François Debret of Suger's stained glass as installed at Saint-Denis by 1842, showing two panels from the lost First Crusade and Pilgrimage of Charlemagne windows (bottom), the Quadriga of Aminadab (center left), and the Annunciation, with Suger at the feet of the Virgin (upper left). After Ferdinand de Lasteyrie

original scenes, that the window originally was composed in a cluster arrangement. Grodecki (1976, 81–92) has presented his interpretation of the original design.

4. Grodecki, 1976, 54–55.

5. *De Administratione*, XXXIV, ed. Panofsky, 1979, 72–77.

6. Mâle, 1978, 171–77; Watson, 1934, 77–82, 112–20; Grodecki, 1976, 71–80, with extensive bibliography.

7. Panofsky, 1979, 203–4.

8. Grodecki, 1961, 19–46, provides the most comprehensive treatment. See also Grodecki, *Artibus*, 1961, 170–86. These ideas are summarized in Grodecki, 1977, 91–102.

9. On this question see Panofsky, 1979, 19–25.

10. On this relationship see Grodecki, 1976, 115–21.

11. Grodecki, *Artibus*, 1961, 22–35.

12. Grodecki, 1976, 103–5, ill. 137.

13. On this question see Grodecki, 1976, 118–19.

14. Grodecki has collected evidence for the various panels from the Saint Benedict window. See Grodecki, 1958, 163–71, and, more recently, Grodecki, 1976, 108–14, ills. 145–63.

15. On the relic see Panofsky, 1979, 205–6. On the location of the matutinal altar see Conway, 1915, 107, and also *De Administratione*, [XXXIII A], ed. Panofsky, 1979, 67–68.

16. Grodecki (1977, 96–100) summarizes his theories on style.

17. Crosby, 1966, 19–30.

18. *De Administratione*, XXXIV, ed. Panofsky, 1979, 72.

19. *De Administratione*, XXXIV, ed. Panofsky, 1979, 76.

20. See note 16.

Figure 28. The Griffin window, Choir, now in the Chapel of Saint Osmana

*10. King, from the Tree of Jesse Window

Choir, Chapel of the Virgin
Pot metal glass with grisaille paint
About 1144
Height, 70 cm. (27½ in.); width, 80 cm. (31½ in.)
Lyons, Musée des Beaux-Arts, D.268

The Tree of Jesse was mentioned by Suger (*De Administratione*, XXXIV, ed. Panofsky, 1979, 72) as the beginning of the series of windows in the chevet of the church. This has been interpreted to mean the window in the central chapel of the choir that was noted by Jacques Doublet in 1625 (246, 359). This panel of a king seated upon the branches of a tree is assumed to have been the first of a series of three kings placed directly above the sleeping figure of Jesse in the window. The drawing made by Percier in 1794–95 does not show the type of costume worn by this figure but the details of collar and girdle, unique to this particular king, are shown in a drawing made for Montfaucon before 1721 (Grodecki, 1976, 170, ill. 36). The figure was not among those exhibited by Lenoir in his Musée des Monuments Français in 1799 nor was it returned to the abbey for reinstallation in 1835 by the architect François Debret. In fact, except for the Montfaucon drawing, nothing is known about this piece until its appearance in private collections in the latter part of the nineteenth century. There is no question, however, as to its authenticity. The figure has been restored twice. The first restoration, which included the head and crown as well as the collar and the belt of the robe, must have taken place before the panel was removed from the choir, since the head of the figure is in the same style as the restored head of the king now occupying the second tier of the tree. A later, careless restoration replaced the feet, the lower trunk of the tree, and part of the background.

The iconography of the Tree of Jesse, inspired by Isaiah 11:1, is no longer considered to have been invented at Saint-Denis (Mâle, 1978, 1–3, n. 80). Elements of this iconography, in embryonic form, appear earlier, especially in Cistercian art. Suger's choir window is, however, the first of a developed type that would persist virtually unchanged until the Late Middle Ages. The Tree of Jesse is a symbolic representation of the genealogy of Christ. At Saint-Denis, the reclining figure of the sleeping Jesse oc-cupied the lowest panel of the window. On the branches of a tree that grew from his side were the seated figures of Christ's royal ancestors, the kings, placed one above the other. At the top of the tree was the Virgin and, above her, Christ surrounded by seven doves, the gifts of the Holy Spirit. Flanking these figures were prophets with scrolls inscribed with their writings related to the Incarnation. Few depictions of the Tree of Jesse prior to Saint-Denis gave such prominence either to the kings or to the tree itself. It has been suggested that the emphasis upon the royal aspects of Christ's ancestry had political overtones (Grodecki, 1977, 95), glorifying the abbey itself and its ties to the French monarchy.

Both nested and parallel folds delineate form in the figure of our king, a common vocabulary in the twelfth century, but there is a softness and a continuous flow to the drapery that is unlike the sharp linearity of the Romanesque style. The figure is well proportioned and articulated. The foliage of the tree is designed with considerable variation of leaf type. The lower leaves droop and curve inward, with delicately painted veins and crosshatched shading of their undersides. The upper leaflets, with their serrated edges, curl about the central bud of the blossom. A jeweled button attaches the blossom to the tendril-like branches of the tree. Pearled bands and the folds of leaf scars decorate these branches. Color ranges toward cool tonalities dominated by the sapphire blue of the background. This precision of detail and elegance of line suggest comparisons with miniatures rather than with monumental art—specifically, with a series of books illuminated at the Cistercian Abbey of Cîteaux in Burgundy during the first half of the twelfth century (cf. Nordenfalk and Grabar, 1958, pl. 155; Porcher, 1959, pls. XXIV, XXV; Dodwell, 1971, pls. 111, 204–6). At least three manuscripts produced at Cîteaux during this period include the Tree of Jesse in various stages of development. Burgundian connections have already been proposed for the sculpture of Saint-Denis (Stoddard, 1952, 52–53) and seem equally valid as origins for the style of the Tree of Jesse Master.

Ex collections: Étienne Duseigneur (Paris); Charles Timbal (Paris); Aymard Collection (Lyons).

Bibliography: Lyons, 1894, no. 117; Grodecki, 1952, 57–61, 1976, 77–79.

11. The Three Magi, from the Infancy of Christ Window

Choir, Chapel of the Virgin
Pot metal glass with grisaille paint
About 1145
Height, 42 cm. (16½ in.); width, 31 cm. (12¼ in.)
Château de Champs-sur-Marne, Dépôt des Monuments Historiques

Though Suger does not mention the Infancy of Christ window in his treatise, its location in the chapel of the Virgin was recorded by both Jacques Doublet and Dom Germain Millet in the seventeenth century (Doublet, 1625, 246; Millet, 1638, 483–84). The figure of Suger at the feet of the Virgin (fig. 1) was engraved for Montfaucon's *Les Monumens de la Monarchie française* in 1720 and the lower portion of the window was included in Percier's sketch of 1794–95. In all probability, the entire window was dismounted by Lenoir in 1799 but only six panels were ever exhibited in his museum in Paris. There is no record of which scenes these were but they were mentioned in general terms by Lenoir (1856, 66) a number of years later. Only three panels were reinstalled by Viollet-le-Duc in 1849, for the rest either had been sold by Lenoir to English collectors or retained by his heirs. The Three Magi was among the latter pieces; it was bought by the state in 1958 after having been, for many years, in the private collection of one of Lenoir's distant relatives.

Viollet-le-Duc had no way of knowing, when he restored the Infancy window, that it was not composed like others at Saint-Denis with registers of panels all of equal height. Grodecki's research has proved, however, that a centralized arrangement of half circles surrounded a central scene. This meant that the scenes above and below the central panel were only half as high, and accounts for the small size of the Three Magi panel. The Three Magi, together with the scene of Herod and His Councillors (cat. no. 12) and a lost panel, formed the register directly above the Nativity that still exists in the window at Saint-Denis.

Each of the three figures in this panel wears a flat, faceted crown similar to those worn by the kings in the Tree of Jesse panel. The central Magus carries a walking stick and the figure on the right points upward, probably at the star that would have appeared in the Adoration panel in the next register above (a fragment of this scene is now in England). Each of the figures seems to be walking toward Herod in the central scene. Between the heads of the Magi is the inscription [MA]GI VENI VNT (*magi*

veniunt, "the Magi come"). The scene is, therefore, from the beginning of the story of the Magi (Matthew 2:1–8) when they have followed the star and are about to ask Herod the whereabouts of the Child Jesus. The lost scene on the right, if it followed the similar arrangement at Chartres, might have been the same three figures departing from Herod's presence. In the full-sized register above would have been three panels devoted to the Adoration. In a narrative window containing only twenty-one scenes, the devotion of six to the saga of the Magi seems excessive. Percier's sketch indicates that certain scenes, such as the Visitation, were omitted from the window. However, the solution to this problem probably relates to the special significance of this window within the iconographic program at Saint-Denis. The Infancy window, unlike the later one at Chartres (cf. Delaporte and Houvet, 1926, pls. I, IV, V), was not a narrative cycle, but a symbolic representation of the miracle of the Incarnation. Scenes essential to this meaning were stressed at the expense of others. An inclusion unique to this window was the placement of Jeremiah, who prophesied the Incarnation, in the first register, as a pendant to Isaiah. (The Jeremiah panel is now in Glasgow; Wells, 1965, no. 2.) In the central medallion, the Magi, as royal visitors, presented their gifts to the Incarnate just as the kings of France had presented relics of Christ's Passion to Saint-Denis. Thus, the special privilege of the abbey and the religious significance of the monarchy were reiterated in the window, and reaffirmed by the inclusion of Suger at the feet of the Virgin in the Annunciation scene (fig. 1).

Though this panel is partly restored, the individual stylistic traits of the Infancy Master are clearly discernible. His three figures have a child-like appearance that is accentuated by their large heads and slender bodies. Their individualized features and lively poses endow them with a naïve charm that is characteristic of this workshop. Drapery is schematically rendered in triangular folds and hangs in stiff, unyielding masses. The small mounds of earth that form the groundline of the scene are a standard device in the twelfth century and are frequently decorated with plants as they are here, but the addition of a band of ornament on the upper edge of the mounds is indicative of this master's fondness for incidental decoration. The glass of the Infancy workshop is more varied and colorful and is thus clearly distinguishable from that of the Tree of Jesse Master.

Bibliography: Grodecki, *Artibus*, 1961, 170–86, 1976, 81–92; Grodecki and Perrot, 1973, no. 1.

12. Herod and His Councillors, from the Infancy of Christ Window

Choir, Chapel of the Virgin
Pot metal glass with grisaille paint
About 1145
Height, 33 cm. (13 in.); width, 50 cm. (19¾ in.)
Château de Champs-sur-Marne, Dépôt des Monuments Historiques

Unlike most of the other glass from the Infancy window, this panel was returned to Saint-Denis after the closing of Lenoir's museum in Paris. It was then installed by Debret in 1844 in the large window above the western portal of the church where it remained until its removal in 1954 by Jules Formigé, then architect in charge of Saint-Denis (Grodecki, 1976, 84). Because this panel was not submitted to the drastic restoration undergone by the choir windows in the nineteenth century, the glass and the paint are in excellent condition and permit a close examination of the style of the Infancy workshop. Only the costume of the councillor on the right and the fillets along the edge of the panel have been replaced.

Herod, seated upon his throne on the left side of the scene, raises his hand to grant audience to the Three Magi of the previous panel (cat. no. 11). He is identified by the name [HE]RODES inscribed beneath his feet. On the right, two of his councillors consult their books to discover the place in which Christ is to be born. In essence, this scene was duplicated in the later Infancy window at Chartres.

Of all the glass painters who worked at the abbey, this master best represents the "international workshop" that created an indigenous style at Saint-Denis. Characteristics previously noted in the style of this master—such as the large-headed figures, individualized facial features, active poses, and heavy, schematized drapery—also apply to this panel. The large, globular eyes, straight noses, luxuriant moustaches, and curled beards are also found on the sculptured heads of earlier figures on the west facade of the church (cat. nos. 1 A,B). The manner in which the hangings of Herod's throne are looped over and swing outward in long parallel pleats is duplicated almost exactly in the drapery of the angels that carry the Passion symbols on the tympanum of the central portal (Crosby and Blum, 1973, pl. IVa). Both the drapery style and the figure type are repeated in the more accomplished carving of the bas-relief of the apostles (cat. no. 6), as are the arcaded sides of the councillors' benches and the embroidered collar and cuffs of Herod's robe. The style of this master is closest to that of the west windows at Chartres, if one allows for the differences in scale. It is for these reasons that we suggest that the origins of this master may have been localized in the Paris area.

Bibliography: Grodecki, *Artibus*, 1961, 170–86, 1976, 81–92; Grodecki and Perrot, 1973, no. 1.

13. The Flight into Egypt, from the Infancy of Christ Window(?)

Choir, Chapel of the Virgin
Pot metal glass with grisaille paint
About 1145
Height, 52 cm. (20½ in.); width, 50 cm. (19¾ in.)

Bryn Athyn, Pennsylvania, The Glencairn Museum,
Academy of the New Church, 03.SG.114

Nothing is known of this panel prior to its acquisition in 1930. Its authenticity has been questioned (Grodecki, 1976, 67), but recent scientific analysis, summarized below, indicates that the evidence should be reviewed. The panel is in excellent condition, not often the case with glass from Saint-Denis, but the back surface exhibits the type of patina characteristic of other glass from the abbey that has been preserved in museums.

If the panel is, in fact, genuine, the first consideration is its placement in the Infancy window at Saint-Denis. On the basis of the Percier drawing and the scenes that he has discovered in collections, Grodecki has reconstructed the Infancy window. This reconstruction is composed of clusters of scenes rather than the alternation of round and square frames employed by Viollet-le-Duc, an arrangement based on the Infancy window at Chartres. The upper portion of Grodecki's reconstructed window is, however, admittedly hypothetical, since much of the glass, including the entire sequence of the Massacre of the Innocents, is missing. The only scene recovered so far is that identified by Grodecki as the Flight into Egypt, now in Wilton Parish Church in England (fig. 29). As reconstructed, the plan of the upper portion of the light does not repeat the arrangement, verified by the Percier drawing, of the lower portion. This is contrary to the general rule for twelfth-century windows, including those at Saint-Denis. Michael Cothren (1978, 74–75), the first to suggest the authenticity of the Bryn Athyn piece, has proposed a new arrangement in which the top portion of the Infancy window repeats in reverse the compartmentalization of the lower part. Based on the scenes included in the Chartres window, admittedly very close in their iconography to those from Saint-Denis (cf. cat. nos. 11, 12), Cothren has proposed that the Wilton Flight is, in reality, the Entrance of the Holy Family into Soutine, mentioned in Pseudo-Matthew XXII and included at Chartres. In his reconstruction, the Bryn Athyn Flight would occupy the central square compartment directly above the Presentation in the Temple as a counterpart to the placement of the rectangular Nativity still *in situ* at Saint-Denis. The Wilton Flight, known from a pre-restoration drawing (fig. 29) made by the glass historian Charles Winston before 1840, was less than two thirds as wide as the central tier of panels at Saint-Denis. It matched, however, the width of the side panels, and, because

of its segmental shape, Cothren has convincingly suggested the placement of the scene in the right-hand curved compartment at the top of the window. The Entrance into Soutine would fill the central compartment as it does at Chartres.

The next problem that must be reviewed is the questioned authenticity of the Bryn Athyn Flight. This must be considered on technical, iconographic, and stylistic grounds.

On the basis of scientific findings, art historians have been reluctant to examine the glass for possible restorations. Part of the evidence that must be considered is historical. A number of panels from the Infancy window were sold directly by Lenoir in 1802 to the English dealer Christopher Hampp (Grodecki, 1976, 4–5). Many of these panels have since been located in English collections; others passed to Lenoir's heirs. The latest discovery (cf. cat. no. 11) was not made until 1958. A large amount of glass in the depot at Saint-Denis was sent to the Gérente atelier in Paris in 1852 (Grodecki, 1976, 52–56). Additional panels, unsuitable for Viollet-le-Duc's restoration, were abandoned to storage. The poor storage conditions and the vulnerability of the panels were remarked upon by François de Guilhermy in 1858. Nothing has ever been recovered from either of these caches and, apparently, the glass gradually or mysteriously disappeared.

Examination of the back surface of the glass shows that most of the pieces appear to be old, a dilemma for the art historian since this is rarely the case in Medieval windows. Most genuine pieces contain replacements in modern glass. In the panel, the edges of the glass pieces that have been removed or that can be seen beneath the leads appear to be grozed in the Medieval manner. The front, painted surface of the glass is, however, quite another matter. There are two distinct colors of paint observable, which would not be the case if the pieces had been painted as a group. The color change, moreover, is so great that it could not be attributed to different batches of paint. The chemical components are evidently very different. Areas such as the bridle of the ass and Joseph's staff, both painted with red-toned paint, have been questioned, and if they are considered as "restoration," then all the other pieces similarly painted are also suspect. Furthermore, most of these pieces are also iconographically questionable.

One element in the iconography of the Flight into Egypt that has been doubted is the unusual inclusion of the bending palm tree that offers its fruit to the Virgin. While this type is known in twelfth-century art, it is extremely rare. Here, it appears to be a parody of the tree in the scene at Chartres. The cask that hangs from Joseph's stick is another questionable item, as is the long blue veil worn by the Virgin. Mary's veil is usually white and short, as it is in the

78

Figure 29. Drawing by Charles Winston of the Flight into Egypt, from the Infancy of Christ window, Choir, Chapel of the Virgin (now in Wilton Parish Church, England). Before 1840

Nativity at Saint-Denis and in the Flight at Chartres. In addition, Joseph's elaborate costume and the cap that does not quite fit on his head are not in keeping with his humble state. These iconographical impossibilities are almost all in red-toned paint.

Further stylistic incongruities must be explained in this panel. The stalk of the central tree and the central leaf frond are carelessly painted. The face of the Virgin, moreover, is painted in the style of the Saint Benedict workshop rather than that of the Infancy Master or any of his assistants. There is no question that the quality of work of the Infancy shop is uneven, or that the master's assistants must have executed many of the scenes in the window, particularly those in its upper parts. However, the style is distinct and not to be confused with that of other ateliers at Saint-Denis.

It is this style that is apparent in certain parts of the Flight into Egypt. The hand, or hands, of the Infancy shop can be seen in the figure of Joseph, except for the hat and the girdle. It can be seen also in the Child, the donkey, and in Mary's skirt. Much of the lower portion of the scene, except for the tree trunk, the background to its right, and the mounds below, seems convincing, and all these parts are painted with a darkish, gray-brown paint. The upper portion of the Virgin including her head and her raised arm and hand, the nimbus of the Child, and the palm tree and striated red background adjoining it should be regarded as restoration, too. Retouching of the original parts with cold enamel must also be considered, especially in comparison with other recovered scenes from the Infancy window. An example of this technique can be seen in the harness of the donkey. The strap on his rump is boldly defined but the pattern is hardly visible, and the strap around his neck has almost disappeared. The latter case must have been an oversight on the part of the restorer.

We are left, therefore, with a fragment, but one that seems far more convincing than the whole. Perhaps it was the fragmentary state of this panel that might account for its abandonment, together with other pieces from the same window, in the restoration by Viollet-le-Duc. Whether the glass lay in the depot at Saint-Denis until it was dispersed or whether it was among the fragments left in the atelier of Gérente will never be known.

The scientific findings, which follow directly below, must also be accounted for. These indicate that the glass tested was not only similar to other glass of the twelfth century but comparable to borders from the Infancy window (cat. no. 14 A,B). The evidence suggests, therefore, that the Flight into Egypt is made from twelfth-century glass that compares chemically with glass made for Suger's choir at Saint-Denis. Art historical evidence cannot argue with scientific fact.

There are circumstances, however, that might explain these findings. This panel was not purchased until 1930, but ten years earlier the American collector Raymond Pitcairn had obtained from the restorer Michel Acezod cartoons of new panels made by Alfred Gérente to complete the Allegories of Saint Paul window at Saint-Denis (fig. 21). Acezod's name is also mentioned in connection with the Flight but he was not the dealer involved in the 1930 sale. It is possible that Acezod somehow acquired the contents of the Gérente atelier, found the fragment among them, and restored the Flight into Egypt with the bits of old glass that Gérente had also received from the depot at Saint-Denis. According to records, this amounted to more than sixteen kilos, including five of red glass—enough to restore the Flight several times over. The weathering on the back of the glass indicates age but it is sometimes uneven, as in the case of the head of the Virgin. At other times it appears false, particularly in the striated red glass on the left side of the panel. Gérente himself apparently did not reemploy old glass in his restorations, but in the thriving art market of the twentieth century this is common practice. Though speculative, these circumstances might explain the mystery of the Flight into Egypt.

Bibliography: Cothren, 1978, 74–75.

Some Chemical Notes

Quantitative chemical analyses have been made of seven small samples of variously colored glasses from the Flight into Egypt window in The Glencairn Museum (Academy of the New Church), and of six samples from the border of the Infancy of Christ window in The Metropolitan Museum of Art. These analyses produced two extremely interesting results. With the single exception of the dark blue glass in the panel, the analyses of the two groups are virtually indistinguishable from one another. The similarity is so close that the glasses could well have been made in the same place, at the same time, for the same building. All of the glasses are of the potash-lime-silica type except for the dark blue of the panel, which is a soda-lime-silica glass. That glass also contains an intentional addition of antimony. These chemical peculiarities link the panel to a small but increasing number of twelfth-century windows that contain dark blue soda glasses together with other colors of the more common potash type. Related examples are from Chartres, Mont-Saint-Michel, and York. Why the dark blue of the panel is a soda glass and the dark blue of the border a potash glass remains a tantalizing question.

Lead-isotope determinations on the minute traces of lead introduced with the cobalt colorant suggest, for the present, that the cobalt came from Persia, possibly from mines in Kamsar or Miskani. Similar experiments on some other twelfth-century dark blue glasses suggest that their cobalt might have come from southern Spain or from Morocco.

Continuing research of this sort should someday establish whether these unusual dark blue soda glasses resulted from a western glassmaking tradition, which can be traced back to Roman times, or whether they are related to somewhat similar glasses from the Byzantine world or the Holy Land.

Dr. Robert H. Brill, Research Scientist
The Corning Museum of Glass

Dr. Lynus Barnes, Research Chemist
National Bureau of Standards

14. Two Fragments of the Border Section, from the Infancy of Christ Window

Choir, Chapel of the Virgin
Pot metal glass with grisaille paint
About 1145
Height, 42.6 cm. (18⅛ in.); width, 11.4 cm. (5½ in.), each
New York, The Metropolitan Museum of Art, 26.28.6a,b

These two pieces were identified by Grodecki (1952, 55–57) as fragments from the Infancy of Christ window. Nothing is known of their history before their acquisition by George Pratt. Each is only half the width of the original border and they are not halves of the same piece. It is Grodecki's opinion (1976, 127) that when the Infancy window was removed by Lenoir in 1799 parts of the border were cut down for installation in his museum. When the museum closed in 1816 the pieces were discarded and sold.

Despite their fragmentary state the pieces are reasonably well preserved, so that it is possible to reconstruct the original design. The border was composed of symmetrical bouquets of foliage sprouting from a trefoil bud and terminating in a trumpet-shaped flower surrounded by a painted ribbon. The lower pair of leaves curls downward within the field formed by the ribbon but the upper pair curves upward and intercepts the strap. The ribbon describes a heart shape around the bouquet and continues to form an interface around a pearled circlet. The interior field of the design is blue and the background red. The complete pattern, of which these two pieces are halves, repeats in opposing motifs joined at the base of the bouquets by a pair of horizontally placed leaves. The design is, therefore, of the centralized type most common to borders of the twelfth century.

Both the ribbon and the circlet designs are scratched out of the paint with a stylus. The ribbon motif is a zigzag while that of the circlet is a series of pearls interspersed with crosses. The veining of the leaves is achieved with fine brushstrokes, sometimes overpainted for emphasis. The undersides of the horizontal leaves and the trumpet flower are cross-hatched. Two tones of mat paint and trace lines delineate form.

The style of this border is much freer than the precise ornamentation of the Tree of Jesse Master. None of its leaf fronds has the pearled veins that are characteristic of the latter's work. However, the Infancy Master was more of a colorist than a draftsman. Within the basic red-and-blue divisions of the background and the secondary tones utilized for the foliage he avoided monotony and created a color accent by making the circlet of yellow glass contrast with the white of the ribbon. Though variants of this border are frequent in twelfth-century windows, the color scheme of these other borders is often simpler and the strapwork invariably white.

Ex collection: George Pratt (New York).

Bibliography: Grodecki, 1952, 55–57, 1976, 88–89, 126–27.

14A

14B

83

15. Border Section, from the Moses Window(?)

Choir, Chapel of Saint Peregrinus
Pot metal glass with grisaille paint
About 1144
Height, 48.8 cm. (19 3/16 in.); width, 22.9 cm. (3 9/16 in.)
Bryn Athyn, Pennsylvania, The Glencairn Museum, Academy of the New Church, 03.SG.181

A border of this design was made by Alfred Gérente for the Moses window in the chapel of Saint Peregrinus in the choir of Saint-Denis during the restoration of the church in 1852. Gérente also copied the same border for the Visions of Ezekiel window (fig. 26) in the chapel of Saint Cucuphas, this time employing a number of original fragments of glass. A third version, somewhat coarser in execution and now included in a composite window in the chapel of Saint Eugène, was probably made by Debret during the earlier restoration of the abbey, from 1816 to 1846. Because of the re-use of the design, it is impossible to determine the original location of this border in the choir of Saint-Denis (Grodecki, 1976, 129–30). That it came from the choir is ascertained by an engraving of the design published by Charles Cahier and Arthur Martin in 1841 (pl. D,b). If Grodecki's reconstruction of the Ezekiel window, based on the Percier drawing (fig. 19) and its accompanying Passion cycle, is correct, this border would have been too wide to have been accommodated in these windows. It is more likely, therefore, to have come from the Moses window.

The width of this border and its vertical orientation of centrally grouped rather than continuously repeated elements are characteristic of stained-glass ornament in the mid-twelfth century. Windows with similarly composed borders are found at Angers, Poitiers, and Chartres. The palmette enclosed by a knotted ribbon or strap, either repeated or opposed as in this example, is one of the most common and widely used ornamental motifs of the twelfth century. It is neither restricted to geographical area nor to medium, and appears both in England and in France on sculpture, metalwork, and in manuscripts, as well as in stained glass. In general, the distinguishing feature of this border and ornament from Saint-Denis is its exceptional richness. Pearls interspersed with tiny pierced beads are incised in the paint of the ribbon. Where strands of ribbon intersect, they are caught with button rosettes. The undersides of the leaves have beaded veins or cross-hatching peculiar to foliate ornament at Saint-Denis from the time of Suger, seen also in the sculpture of the facade (cat. no. 2B), on the bas-relief of the apostles (cat. no. 6), and on metalwork (cat. no. 27), as well as in glass.

Only one other border design known from Saint-Denis has the width or the complexity of this example. The actual piece has since disappeared (Grodecki, 1976, ill. 198), but, as is apparent in the tracing with color notation made by Just Lisch in 1850, the intricately woven ribbon, the pearling of the leaf veins, and, most of all, the button rosettes that catch the strands of ribbon compare only to our example. If our border can be accepted as having come from the Moses window, then this second lost piece indicates that other windows by the hand of this master were included in Suger's choir and have disappeared without a trace.

The origins of this richly ornamental style may well lie eastward in the Rhineland and the Meuse, where the tradition of fine metalwork employing these techniques was well-known even in Suger's time (Crosby, 1966, 24–27). That this master was familiar with such techniques is exemplified by his ornament, as shown in this border. If he was not trained as a goldsmith, he was certainly influenced by the other crafts produced at Saint-Denis.

Bibliography: Gómez-Moreno, 1968, no. 175; Grodecki, 1976, 129, ill. 200.

85

*16. The Quadriga of Aminadab, from the Allegories of Saint Paul Window

Choir, Chapel of Saint Peregrinus
Pot metal glass with grisaille paint
About 1144
Diameter, 67 cm. (26½ in.)
Cathedral of Saint-Denis

This panel is one of those discussed in detail by Suger (*De Administratione*, XXXIV, ed. Panofsky, 1979, 74–75). It was placed in the central compartment in what he described as a window "urging us onward from the material to the immaterial" and what Panofsky has called the "Anagogical window" (1979, 20–21). Grodecki has interpreted the symbolism of this window as deriving from allegories contained in the Epistles of Saint Paul. The window was mentioned in general terms in the seventeenth century and specifically in the eighteenth century (Lebeuf, 1754, III, 182–83). Percier included it in his sketch of 1794–95, from which we can determine both the original design of the window and its border. The two panels surviving from this window were exhibited by Lenoir in his museum in 1799 and were later installed by Debret in the chapel of the Virgin at Saint-Denis (fig. 27). Viollet-le-Duc restored the window in 1852 with a border and new scenes, based on Suger's inscriptions, which were designed by Alfred Gérente (fig. 21). The glass was placed in the chapel of Saint Peregrinus where it probably had been located originally, in Suger's time.

Grodecki has undertaken extensive research on the iconography of this window (1961, 19–35). As he notes, since its iconography is taken from Saint Paul, the window is a direct reminder, on Suger's part, of the connection thought to exist between the abbey's patron and the apostle who, supposedly, was his teacher. The so-called Quadriga of Aminadab is, perhaps, the most abstruse of the group. As Grodecki states, the composition itself is a kind of sacred hieroglyph where each element stands out, because of its isolation, against the void of the background. In the center of the scene is the golden quadriga with four wheels, two of which are placed above and two below the body of the cart. Its side is decorated with a filigree pattern imitating metalwork (see cat. no. 25). Within this golden chariot, now partly restored, the tablets of Moses and Aaron's rod could once be seen (cf. Cahier and Martin, 1841–44, I, pl. ET.VI, F). Behind the quadriga is the figure of God holding the crucified Christ on the cross. It is the *Crux viridis*, the green living cross, and it, too, is painted in filigree, like metalwork. In the quadrants of the circular panel are the symbols of the four Evangelists: the angel of Matthew, the eagle of John, the lion of Mark, and the ox of Luke. In the center of the panel is the inscription recorded by Suger: FEDERIS • EX • ARCA • C RVCE • /XRISISTITVR • ARA/FEDERE • MAIORI • VVLT • IBIVITA/MORI • ("On the Ark of the Covenant is established the altar with the Cross of Christ;/Here Life wishes to die under a greater covenant." *De Administratione*, XXXIV, ed. Panofsky,

1979, 75). At the bottom of the panel, the ark is designated: QVADRIGE•/AMINADAB• .

The symbolic significance of this scene is to be found in Paul's Epistle to the Hebrews, chapters 9 and 10, where the New Alliance between God and mankind is explained. The ark of gold containing the rod of Aaron and the tablets of the Law is the altar of the Old Testament. It becomes the altar of Christ through his sacrifice on the cross. The First Alliance occurred when Moses, by asperging the people with the blood of animal sacrifice, expiated their sins against God. The Second Alliance took place when Christ offered his own blood to God as a sacrifice for mankind. In this panel, therefore, the cross of Christ, the new Law, is placed by God upon the altar of the old Law in recognition of the New Alliance. The inscription "Quadrige Aminadab" also has significance for the meaning of the scene. In the Song of Solomon 6:12, the Shunammite wonders why she is troubled at being placed in the chariot of Aminadab. The chariot in this passage was identified by the early Church fathers as the new chariot, made by the grandsons of Aminadab, to transport the Holy Ark to Jerusalem (Exodus 6:23). Since there is also a reference in Habakkuk 3:8 to the quadriga as salvation, the chariot symbolized the Christian Church. The Shunammite was, therefore, seen as the Synagogue, which was carried upon the Church. The four wheels of the chariot are the four Gospels and the four symbols of the tetramorph are their authors, the Evangelists. In order to clarify this meaning, the quadriga in the panel is represented illogically, with its wheels placed above, rather than behind, the ark.

Perhaps more graphically exemplified in other windows by this master—such as the Life of Moses—but also evident in this panel is his expressive figure style. The symbols of the Evangelists, in the quadrants of the circle, create a dynamic tension with the horizontal and vertical equilibrium of the central group. They seem to be projected by an unseen force toward the cross at the center of the composition. In contrast to the icon-like God the Father, the Evangelists are animated and expressive.

Most outstanding in the work of this master are the comparisons that can be made with metalwork, particularly with the vessels made for Suger at Saint-Denis. Both the pattern of rinceaux on the side of the ark, with its beaded edging, and the double vine scroll of the cross are to be found on Suger's Chalice (cat. no. 25). Even the inscriptions are embellished with ornament. That this master could so accurately reproduce these patterns in painted glass presupposes a familiarity with goldsmithing. If this artist had not, in fact, been trained as a goldsmith, he had certainly devoted careful study to the techniques of metalwork. This panel was made by a craftsman who was also a master of design and of the art of stained glass.

Bibliography: Grodecki, 1961, 19–46, 1976, 93–102; Hoffmann, 1968, 57–88.

17. The Death of Saint Benedict Witnessed by Two Monks, from the Saint Benedict Window

Crypt, Chapel of Saint Benedict
Pot metal glass with grisaille paint
About 1145
Height, 60 cm. (23⅝ in.); width, 38 cm. (15 in.)
Paris, Musée de Cluny, CL 22758

Neither Suger nor any seventeenth- or eighteenth-century historian mentions windows devoted to the life of Saint Benedict at the Abbey of Saint-Denis, a member of the order that he founded. Suger does, however, record that there was a chapel dedicated to the saint in the crypt of the new choir (*De Consecratione*, VII, ed. Panofsky, 1979, 118–19). Percier's drawing of 1794–95 (fig. 19) records the border and ornament of the window with the two monks, proving without question that the window originated at Saint-Denis. This particular panel was still at the abbey in 1850, when Just Lisch traced it (fig. 20 a). The panel was not reincorporated in the restoration of the abbey by Viollet-le-Duc but must have been abandoned in the atelier of the restorer, Alfred Gérente, since the panel was purchased by the state in 1958 from the private collection of one of Gérente's relatives. A number of other panels from this window have been discovered by Grodecki in collections in England, France, and the United States.

One of the questions concerning the Saint Benedict window is its original location in the church. Grodecki (1976, 112–14) believes that, when drawn by Percier, the window was installed in the choir, but that this was a reinstallation of the glass that was originally in the chapel of Saint Benedict in the crypt. His calculations of the size of the window confirm this theory. The problem is that so much glass has been recovered from this window (one complete scene, four half panels, and two fragments) that it could not be accommodated in a single aperture in the crypt. At best, the crypt windows would only hold three scenes. There are, however, two windows of the same dimensions in the chapel of Saint Benedict. Grodecki's solution is that both windows in the chapel were filled with scenes from the saint's life. Unlike the windows in the choir of Saint-Denis, the scenes of Saint Benedict were divided into two panels by a vertical iron support, not an uncommon type of armature in the twelfth century. Because of its subject and because part of the border cuts across the upper left corner, the Cluny panel was the left half of the topmost scene in one of the crypt windows.

Though the inscription has been reinserted in the panel from the edging of the border that was originally placed directly above, the piece is in an excellent state of preservation. Only the middle section of the robe of the monk at the left has been replaced. That the inscription initially belonged with this scene is confirmed by its meaning. Though missing in part, it reads: hec est via qva dilec tvs domin o beat[vs er]at erbenedic[tvs coelvm ascendit] ("This is the path by which the beloved of God, the blessed brother Benedict, ascended to heaven"). According to legend (Mabillon, 1668, III, 287), at the moment of Benedict's death a celestial messenger appeared to two of his monks and showed them a vision of a luminous path leading from Benedict's cell up to heaven. In the Cluny panel the two monks gaze upward, while the missing right half of the scene probably depicted the ray of light issuing from the cell of the saint. This scene and others that have been discovered from the window indicate that it contained a purely narrative account of Saint Benedict's life, unlike the highly symbolic windows and interrelated iconographic program devised for the choir.

The style of the Saint Benedict Master is distinctive and quite dissimilar to that of the other ateliers that worked in the choir. His figures, as exemplified by the two monks, are extremely elongated, with small heads and tiny claw-like hands. Little attempt is made to indicate the form or movement of the figures beneath their garments. Drapery either hangs in long, absolutely straight pleats or in a series of diagonal V-shaped folds. The preferred silhouette for his figures is a long rectangle. Gestures are restricted and the arms are held close to the body. The eyes are the distinctive feature of his faces—large and round, terminating at the outer corners with two short lines separating the upper from the lower lid. The mouths are small and bow-like.

As with most of the other shops that worked at Saint-Denis, the Saint Benedict Master profusely decorated his work. The two monks stand upon mounds of earth delicately painted with a field of flowers. This panel is one of the few from Saint-Denis in which the ornamental field has been preserved. One can observe in this example the painted frame of the scene composed of two bands of pearls with foliate ornament between them. As shown in Percier's drawing, this type of decorative frame was utilized in all the glass at Saint-Denis. The lower left-hand corner is filled with a quarter circle of ornament whose fluted center is not unlike designs employed in metalwork at Saint-Denis (cat. no. 26). Grodecki (1958, 165–66) has compared the figure style of the Saint Benedict Master to that of manuscript illumination in the north of France at the Abbey of Saint-Bertin at Saint-Omer. Comparisons can also be made with certain manuscripts emanating from the scriptorium at Mont-Saint-Michel even further west (cf. Alexander, 1970, 85–86, pl. 17B). However, the work of the Saint Benedict atelier bears no comparisons with any contemporary stained glass in northwestern France. Similarities are isolated and limited to a few examples, so that the precise origins of this shop have yet to be defined.

Bibliography: Grodecki, 1958, 161–71, 1976, 108–14.

see Frontispiece

18. Border Section, from the Saint Benedict Window

Crypt, Chapel of Saint Benedict
Pot metal glass with grisaille paint
About 1145
Height, 36 cm. (14¼ in.); width, 15 cm. (5⅞ in.)
Bryn Athyn, Pennsylvania, The Glencairn Museum, Academy of the New Church, 03.SG.33

Percier recorded the design of the border of the Saint Benedict window in 1794–95. Just Lisch traced this section of the border (fig. 20b) in 1850, while the glass was still at Saint-Denis. Viollet-le-Duc did not reinstall the window during his restoration of the abbey, nor did he copy its border design for any other window. This piece was probably stored at the abbey or in the workshop of Alfred Gérente in Paris and later sold. Nothing further is known about it until its purchase by the American collector Raymond Pitcairn in the 1920s.

The piece is in excellent condition with few replacements. It has even retained the slight curve toward the right of the upper palmette and the outer-edge fillet that locates its original position in the window. This border section was originally aligned along the lower left-hand edge of the Cluny panel (cat. no. 17) and extended as far as the top of the panel, following the curvature of the window frame. The curved top of the piece was probably cut off at some point in its history to make it a more salable item. In addition to the segment attached to the Cluny panel, three other pieces of this border have been identified in collections in Paris and the United States (Grodecki, 1976, ill. 203; Gómez-Moreno, 1968, nos. 176, 177) and an additional fragment is at The Cloisters (unpublished).

The design is simpler than the borders of the choir windows. Each palmette is enclosed by a vine stem from which curling leaves sprout. The interior bouquets are symmetrically arranged, with two pairs of leaves in alternating colors of pink and yellow from one cluster to the next. Motifs are connected by a looped knot in the vine. The interior field is blue, the vine white, and the background green. Predominantly cool colors in the border contrast with the red background of the window. The painting technique is less elegant than that of the choir windows and the leaves are somewhat stiffly drawn. The pearls on the undersides of the leaves are not overpainted with mat as they are in the Moses border, so the curvilinear effect of these leaves is lessened in much the same way that the schematic design of the drapery flattens the figures in the Saint Benedict window scenes.

Bibliography: Grodecki, 1958, 161–71, 1976, 112–14, 127, ill. 203; Gómez-Moreno, 1968, nos. 176, 177.

*19. The Martyrdom of Saint Vincent, from the Saint Vincent Window

Crypt
Pot metal glass with grisaille paint
About 1145
Diameter, 46 cm. (18 in.)
Château de Champs-sur-Marne, Dépôt des Monuments Historiques

The existence of this panel in the second radiating chapel on the north side of the choir was noted by two nineteenth-century historians before Viollet-le-Duc's restoration of Saint-Denis (Guilhermy, 1844, I, fol. 84; de Lasteyrie, 1857, I, 35). The chapel had been rededicated to Saint Vincent in the nineteenth century and contained this panel together with scenes from the saint's life formerly in the Lady Chapel of Saint-Germain-des-Prés in Paris (and now in The Metropolitan Museum). All of the glass in this chapel, which had been returned to Saint-Denis by Lenoir in 1816 and installed by Debret, was removed in 1848 by Viollet-le-Duc and placed in the abbey's storage depot. It was recovered by the Monuments Historiques when the depot was liquidated in 1895.

Until the nineteenth century there was no chapel at Saint-Denis dedicated to Saint Vincent, so that the original location of the window from which this panel came is problematical. From the ninth century, however, the abbey had possessed an important relic of the saint—his arm—that had been presented to the church by Dagobert, the first French king to be buried at Saint-Denis. Even in Suger's time the relic had reposed in the matutinal altar, located at the entrance to the stalls in the Romanesque nave (Panofsky, 1979, 187–88). Suger's reluctance to disturb the older parts of the church, which tradition claimed had been dedicated by Christ himself, may

account for the fact that the relic was never moved to a new chapel dedicated to the saint. That this relic had been presented by Dagobert and that Suger's aim was to promote the power of Saint-Denis through the abbey's royal connections would have been adequate reason to include the life of Saint Vincent in a window. The small size of this panel suggests that the window to which it belonged would have been placed in the crypt and that it was composed of two vertical rows of scenes.

The effect of the panel is very different from its original form since the painted surface has deteriorated and much of the paint has disappeared, leaving light areas, while the unpainted parts are heavily patinated. Although what one sees today is virtually a reverse image of the original, the piece is a remarkable stylistic and technical achievement. Grodecki has estimated that there are more than 180 pieces of glass in this panel in comparison to the one hundred in the Moses scenes. The accuracy of these cuts—for example, in the shoulders and arms of the figure on the right and in the gratings of the grill—is extraordinary. One of the most unusual features of this panel is the delineation of the muscles of the nude saint. Panofsky (1979, 195) was the first to note the resemblance between this nude figure and the Atlantids carved on the doorframe of the right portal of the west facade at Saint-Denis. Not only is the Saint Vincent panel the work of the Infancy shop, which is assured by the figure types and by the variety of colors employed, but it is the work of the master himself, at his peak of achievement. Analogies between the sculpture at the abbey and the work of this master have been cited previously (cf. cat. no. 12) but no example is more convincing than this panel.

Bibliography: Grodecki, 1953, no. 3, 1976, 106–7; Beyer and Grodecki, 1965, no. 176; Panofsky, 1979, 195.

20. The March of the Christian Army, from the First Crusade Window

Choir, Ambulatory Chapel
Pot metal glass with grisaille paint
About 1150
Diameter, 50.1 cm. (19¾ in.)
Bryn Athyn, Pennsylvania, The Glencairn Museum,
Academy of the New Church, 03.SG.156

A window describing the First Crusade, located in the choir of the abbey church, was mentioned by Montfaucon in 1730. As early as 1721, however, drawings of ten panels from this window had been made for him. Lenoir (1818, 30, pl. XXIII) had mentioned one scene and reproduced it a century later. Neither author stated specifically within which chapel the window was located. From the Percier drawing of 1794–95, which, in Grodecki's opinion, includes this window, and from Grodecki's studies of the locations of other glass in the choir, he has concluded that the window occupied the first radiating chapel, on either the north or south side of the choir. Montfaucon reproduced only ten scenes, none of which is from this panel, but Grodecki has calculated that at least fourteen were included in the original design. The earliest record of this particular scene comes from an engraving published by Ferdinand de Lasteyrie (1857, II, pl. III) of the two windows installed by Debret in the chapel of the Virgin in 1833. The scene is shown in the lower right-hand corner of the engraving (fig. 27). It is not known whether this panel was among those removed by Lenoir but it is the only scene now remaining from a window that was not only a work of art but also an important historical document. The panel was evidently not re-used by Viollet-le-Duc in his restoration of 1847 and was probably retired to storage at Saint-Denis, from which it later disappeared. Nothing further is known about this piece until its purchase by Raymond Pitcairn in the 1920s.

From the Percier drawing, Grodecki has postulated that the Crusade window was composed of two vertical rows of circular scenes surrounded by rings of pearled ornament. A narrow border of foliage and ribbons completed the design. Fragments of this border still exist (Grodecki, 1976, 115–21, ill. 208). The head and lower portion of the king, who occupies the center of our remaining scene from the window, and the body of his mount have undergone considerable restoration. Both the inscription band and the glass below it have been replaced. In 1857 de Lasteyrie recorded the letters VLP/IAN/VSIN at the bottom of the piece. Although the last part is still intact, the first part of the inscription is missing, indicating that this portion of the panel had been replaced even in de Lasteyrie's time.

Several suggestions have been offered as to the subject of the scene. The king and his warriors are on the march rather than engaged in battle, as is the case with most of the other panels from this window according to the existing drawings. Grodecki has suggested that the scene might represent the Lotharingian crusaders of Godfrey of Bouillon or the march of the Christian armies across Asia Minor after the battle of Dorylaeum. It is also possible that the scene came from the other window in the same chapel and might represent Charlemagne's army on the way to Constantinople, but this idea can be rejected on the basis of style. Of all the windows of the choir, within the iconographic program these two were the most directly related to the abbey and the monarchy. They served as historic reminders of the role of the French kings as protectors of the abbey. In 1147, just three years after the choir was completed, Louis VII accepted the sacred battle standard from Suger's own hand to carry in a Second Crusade to free the Holy Land. It is obvious that the Crusade window was propaganda for this endeavor.

There is little doubt that this panel was part of the twelfth-century glazing of the choir or that it is a later work by the Infancy workshop, whose short figure type with large globular eyes is exemplified by the warriors. A similar characteristic of this shop that can also be seen in this panel is its use of color. A scene of riders on horseback, all dressed in the same type of armor, could be monotonous, but the master who designed this panel constructed each horse in the group, and its rider, from different colors of glass. The scene is, therefore, animated by small spots of color, a technique that is repeated in the foreground of the composition. The groundline is composed of small hillocks painted with foliage patterns, as was the case in the Three Magi panel (cat. no. 11). The dragon that floats above the figures is, unfortunately, not original. In all probability, it replaced a battle flag, a common feature shown in the lost scenes as recorded by the Montfaucon drawings. A new element in this panel and in the drawings is the change in scale of the compositions. Whereas, in the Infancy window, each scene had only a few figures, in the roundels depicting the Crusade many figures are included. This latter condition was undoubtedly dictated by the subject matter, but the way in which the scenes were composed is an indication of the artistry of the master. In our roundel the warriors are clustered in tight groups in which a single action is repeated. Isolated between two similar groupings of soldiers is the single figure of the king, who thus assumes importance in the scene. The resulting balance achieved is a compositional device that is characteristic of this workshop.

Bibliography: Grodecki, 1976, 115–21.

21. A Triple Coronation, from the Pilgrimage of Charlemagne Window

Choir, Ambulatory Chapel
Pot metal glass with grisaille paint
About 1150
Diameter, 52.3 cm. (20⅝ in.)
Bryn Athyn, Pennsylvania, The Glencairn Museum,
Academy of the New Church, 03.SG.111

Were it not for the French historian Montfaucon, who published his history of the French monarchy in 1730, there would be no record of the Charlemagne window from Saint-Denis. In 1721, Montfaucon had drawings made that were later engraved for his book. Among them were two scenes from the life of Charlemagne, which he noted as having come from one of the choir windows. Percier's sketch of 1794–95 also records two windows that Grodecki believes were those of Charlemagne and the First Crusade, and which, he deduced, had glazed one of the two end chapels of the ambulatory (Grodecki, 1976, 115). The first indication of the Triple Coronation panel was a plate in de Lasteyrie's book (1857, II, pl. III) that depicted Debret's restored windows of 1833 in the chapel of the Virgin (fig. 27). The panel was not reemployed by Viollet-le-Duc and nothing more is known of it until it was purchased in the 1920s by Raymond Pitcairn. There is little doubt, on stylistic and iconographic grounds, that it was originally part of the Charlemagne window at Saint-Denis.

Percier's sketch shows only a detail of the ornamental arrangement of the Charlemagne window, but, on the basis of the size of the one remaining scene, Grodecki has calculated that both the Charlemagne window and its pendant, the History of the First Crusade, were composed of two vertical rows of scenes, fourteen in all. The sketch appears to be a composite view of both windows since Percier indicates two different types of framing for the scenes and shows one window with ornament and another with figures between panels. As a further distinction that two different windows were included on his plan he wrote "another" next to the drawing. From these notations Grodecki has drawn his conclusions. Percier recorded only one border design but there is reason to believe that two different designs existed.

Since only two drawings and one panel of glass remain from the Charlemagne window its iconography is difficult to determine. It can only be interpreted in relation to the legend fabricated at Saint-Denis by 1124 in order to authenticate the abbey's relics of the Passion. These relics had been given to Saint-Denis by the Carolingian Emperor Charles the Bald in the ninth century. According to the legend, Charlemagne had journeyed to the Holy Land with his army and had been received at Constantinople by the Emperor Constantine. While there, Charlemagne had been given the relics by Constantine and had taken them back to his Palatine Chapel at Aachen. His son, Charles the Bald, had then given them to the Abbey of Saint-Denis.

The window appears to have been an elaboration on this legend and others. The inscriptions preserved on the two engraved scenes that Montfaucon published help to determine their subjects. One shows Charlemagne greeted by Constantine at the gates of Constantinople. The other depicts Charlemagne receiving three of Constantine's ambassadors in Paris. The Triple Coronation panel, because it has lost its inscription, is the most difficult to decipher. Though a number of explanations have been offered (Grodecki, 1976, 121) the most logical seems to be that it depicts the Accord of 842, or the Oaths of Strassburg. Charlemagne broke with tradition by dividing his empire, upon his death, into three parts, each of which would be ruled by one of his sons. In the panel are nine figures divided into three groups. The lateral figures wear crowns while the central group is being crowned by the hand of God. In each case, three figures sit upon a single throne. Thus, both the unity and the partitioning of the empire are expressed in this scene. Like the Crusade window, the Charlemagne window symbolized the power and prestige of the abbey.

The Triple Coronation panel and the two engravings of other scenes from the Charlemagne window indicate a change in scale from the Crusade window. The figures are now larger in relation to the field and there is a vertical rather than a horizontal stress to the composition. Both in figure type and in composition the Triple Coronation scene is more like the panels of the Infancy window, although the heads and the rendering of the drapery display a certain stylistic stereotyping also seen in the Crusade window. Only the heads on the left side of the panel are original. The central group of heads is thought to be a thirteenth-century restoration and the ones on the right were replaced in the nineteenth century. (The originals are now in a copy of this panel in Turin.) The heads on the left exactly duplicate in mirror image those from the right-hand side of the scene (now in Turin). One can envision that the Infancy shop had either evolved a formula of representation or that a less-accomplished assistant had succeeded the master.

Bibliography: Grodecki, 1976, 115–21.

22. Border Section, from an Unknown Window

Choir
Pot metal glass with grisaille paint
About 1150
Height, 49.2 cm. (19⅜ in.); width, 12 cm. (4¾ in.)

Bryn Athyn, Pennsylvania, The Glencairn Museum, Academy of the New Church, 03.SG.6

Though its design was not reproduced by Percier, Just Lisch made a tracing of this border section at Saint-Denis about 1850 during the restoration of the choir by Viollet-le-Duc. That the Lisch tracing (fig. 20c) reproduced this exact piece can be determined by the duplication of mending leads, the size, and by the way the design breaks at the top and bottom of the panel. There appears to be little doubt that it was once part of a window at Saint-Denis but there is no documentation to determine which window this might have been. Though there is some restoration in the upper part of the background, and the paint is rubbed in places, the piece is generally in good condition.

Unlike most of the borders at Saint-Denis, but like the Saint Benedict window, this border is not designed with opposing motifs. The pattern of circlets entwined with leaf sprays continues in a single direction. The shapes of these leaves and the painting of the veins with fine brushstrokes recall the leaves in the border of the Infancy window (cat. no. 14A,B). Another element used in both borders is the circlet. In this border, however, the pearling of the circlet is painted rather than scratched out, as in the Infancy window. In neither case, moreover, are there pearled veins in the leaves, almost a hallmark in other windows in the choir.

Also unlike most of the borders at Saint-Denis, this one is very narrow. The only other example of similar dimension is the restored fragment (in storage) that Grodecki has attributed on the basis of the Percier drawing to either the Crusade or the Charlemagne window. Percier does not indicate whether both windows had the same border but if this were true it would be unique for twelfth-century windows. We would suggest that, based on stylistic similarities with the ornament in the Infancy window—whose master also created the Charlemagne and Crusade windows—this border came from one of the latter windows. Neither the two scenes that remain from these windows (cat. nos. 20, 21) nor this border is as skillfully executed as the Infancy window and may be the work of a less-talented assistant.

Bibliography: Grodecki, 1976, 130.

For the Service of the Table of God[1]

Liturgical Objects

The history, from Late Medieval times, of the altar furnishings that Suger added to or had embellished for Saint-Denis is incorporated in the extensive recent account of the entire treasury published by Blaise de Montesquiou-Fezensac with the collaboration of Danielle Gaborit-Chopin.[2] This study, which corrected and expanded the important article by Martin Conway,[3] is based on a careful rereading of the inventories, particularly the most complete one dating from 1634, along with other accounts that predated the French Revolution such as Dom Germain Millet's on the treasury (1645) and Jacques Doublet's and Dom Michel Félibien's histories of the abbey (1625 and 1706, respectively). Félibien's publication of five large engravings of the armoires in which the treasury was displayed during the eighteenth century (figs. 30, 31), and the sketches, color drawings (fig. 35), and notes by Nicolas de Peiresc from the early seventeenth century, have been the prime source material for renewed analyses of the contents of the treasury, specifically those portions of it that were added as a result of Suger's efforts.

The tragic losses were extensive, especially in the sixteenth century and at the time of the French Revolution at the end of the eighteenth century, and devastating to a full understanding of Suger's contributions to the treasury. Two particularly ambitious projects that Suger described with pride have almost if not entirely disappeared. The first, the Great Cross of gold, gems, and enamel,[4] which he had set up between 1145 and 1147 in the new elevated choir and had had embellished by "several goldsmiths from Lorraine," was partially dismembered in the sixteenth century and mostly lost during the seventeenth century; by the Revolution it had entirely vanished. The inventory of 1634 gives a fairly detailed description of the Great Cross with its square supporting column, whose pedestal was adorned with figures of the four Evangelists and enameled plaques with figurative subjects.[5] The pedestal rested upon four dragons. The capital with figures, at the top of the column, was also adorned with enamels, possibly purely decorative ones. Several enamels by Mosan artists have been proposed as remnants of this ensemble, although without universal acceptance.[6]

The second great loss, Le Tombeau des Corps-Saints, was the shrine for the relics of Saints Denis, Rusticus, and Eleutherius, a composite work with an altar, tomb, and tabernacle of stone, copper gilt, and gems (see cat. no. 24). Erected by Suger in the east end of the new choir in 1144, this elaborate structure was badly damaged in the pillage of Saint-Denis in 1567, only to be entirely replaced in 1627 by a Baroque altar

Figure 33 (detail)

Figure 30. Engraving of one of the five eighteenth-century armoires containing the treasure of Saint-Denis, from Dom Michel Félibien's *Histoire de l'abbaye royale de Saint-Denys en France* (1706). The Carolingian crystal once part of Le Tombeau des Corps-Saints (see cat. no. 24) is shown at the top (D), and Suger's Chalice (cat. no. 25) appears in the foreground (R)

that was later destroyed during the Revolution. Reconstructions of Suger's shrine vary according to the interpretations of the abbot's descriptions,[7] subsequent inventories, and the notes and sketches of Peiresc.[8] The tabernacle, or upper portion of Suger's shrine, has provided the only preserved elements in precious materials: several antique gems[9] and the large crystal of Charles the Bald (cat. no. 24), each of which Suger's artists had adapted from the earlier Carolingian shrine also dedicated to the patron saint and his companions. The destruction of these two important monuments, the Great Cross and Le Tombeau des Corps-Saints, is symbolic of the many other losses of precious furnishings from the sanctuary in the choir of the abbey.

Sumner Crosby[10] has underscored the international character of the artist-craftsmen whom Suger gathered at Saint-Denis. While it is difficult to prove the origins of the authors of specific works, the stylistic impact of far-flung traditions on the architecture, sculpture, stained glass, and metalwork has been repeatedly acknowledged by art historians. Normandy, Burgundy, Languedoc, and the valleys of the Meuse and Rhine are the chief art-producing regions beyond the Île-de-France reflected one way or another in Suger's projects. That new indigenous styles were initiated at Saint-Denis is supported by the occasional similarities that not only developed a certain cohesiveness within a single medium but cut across and partially affected all media (see page 67).

Within the area of goldsmiths' work we are confronted with several special circumstances. First, Suger retained and refurbished works from his predecessors: from the Merovingian period, the aventurine Incense Boat (the "Vase of Saint Éloi," cat. no. 23), and from the Carolingian period, the lost Altar Frontal of Charles the Bald (fig. 32). Second, he imported artists to work on entirely new creations, such as the Great Cross. Third, from different sources he acquired hard-stone vessels and had them embellished and bejeweled with silver-gilt mounts and dedicated with inscriptions (cat. nos. 25, 26; fig. 36). The shared technical and stylistic details evident in three of these adaptations presuppose a workshop at Saint-Denis. The technical differences from clearly identifiable Mosan and Rhenish metalwork suggest the possibility that Suger enlisted the efforts of local artists.[11]

Figure 31. Engraving of another of the five eighteenth-century armoires that contained the treasure of Saint-Denis, from Dom Michel Félibien's *Histoire de l'abbaye royale de Saint-Denys en France* (1706). In the foreground (EE, E, and CC, respectively) are Suger's Eagle Vase (fig. 33), Ewer (cat. no. 26), and the Incense Boat known as the "Vase of Saint Éloi" (cat. no. 23; fig. 34)

Suger had a passion for acquiring and reemploying ancient cameos, intaglios, and figured and smooth hard-stone containers. This interest was in keeping with continuing Medieval ideas of permanence and beauty in relation to the flawless appearance of those works preserved from earlier times. Such objects were appreciated and valued within a perceived and established divine order of the universe.[12] Integrity or perfection, consonance of parts, symmetry, clarity, and luminosity were primary considerations in categorizing the beautiful.[13] The amuletic or pagan magical functions of objects were absorbed and superseded by their adaptation to Christian usage. The ancient gem or vessel was carefully preserved intact in the process of this adaptation and change of function. These Medieval principles were already evident in the (now lost) Merovingian mounting of the Incense Boat of Saint Éloi, which Suger acquired as a complete ensemble (cat. no. 23). Suger's artists continued this adaptive process with special brilliance in the instance of the ancient porphyry vase transformed into an eagle vase for the altar (fig. 33).[14] The same principles are evident in the agate Chalice and the sardonyx Ewer (cat. nos. 25, 26).

The purpose of all of Suger's artistic endeavors was aligned with the idea of making Saint-Denis in its structure and content a truly magnificent and radiant royal abbey that would glorify God, pay homage to the saints, and enhance the centralized political power of the Capetian monarchy. The alliance of Louis VI and Suger was strong; Suger established— and the king supported—the supremacy of Saint Denis as the patron saint of France and its monarch. The abbey was confirmed as the repository of the Banner of Saint Denis,[15] which Louis VI and all subsequent kings carried into battle. From Merovingian times onward, some of the royal crowns had been placed in the abbey. Suger, on the basis of his own reading of a deposition charter of 1120 by Louis VI, made legal claim to all of the royal crowns for the abbey. By the end of the twelfth century this claim was extended to include the coronation regalia, which, from then on, was kept at Saint-Denis, in readiness for temporary removal to Rheims for each coronation ceremony.

This tradition was buttressed by the custom of burying French monarchs at Saint-Denis. The practical need to accommodate not only the

Figure 32. Master of Saint Giles. *The Mass of Saint Giles*. French, late fifteenth century. London, National Gallery. The Carolingian Altar Frontal of Charles the Bald may be seen in the painting, adapted as an altarpiece. Suger added sides and a back panel to the altar frontal, which are not shown here. (The altar frontal and Suger's additions are now lost)

royal tombs but also a multitude of people, in order to fulfill its reaffirmed function as a great pilgrimage church,[16] was accompanied by an equally burning requirement to enrich the furnishings of the altars in the sanctuary of the new choir and to make the sacred relics visible in a new and prominent setting nearby.[17]

Panofsky, von Simson, Grodecki, Verdier, and others have written extensively on the sources of Suger's theological and cosmological positions in relation to his anagogical method and to his particular versions of Medieval aesthetics and the metaphysics of light. Suger's theological concepts were dependent upon the ideas of Neoplatonism as interpreted by Saint Augustine (354–430), Pseudo-Dionysius the Areopagite (sixth century), Saint Maximus the Confessor (c. 580–662), Johannes Scotus Erigena (810–877), and by his contemporary and friend Hugh of Saint Victor (d. 1141).[18]

Suger's oft-quoted inscription on the golden doors of the west facade serves as a noble introduction to both his anagogical thought and his new abbey:

> Marvel not at the gold and the expense but at the craftsmanship of the work.
> Bright is the noble work; but, being nobly bright, the work
> Should brighten the minds, so that they may travel, through the true lights,
> To the True Light where Christ is the true door.[19]

Inside the abbey and in his luminous new sanctuary Suger's obsession with the symbolism of light was intensified by the pervasive interior light and the radiant stained glass, as well as by the resplendent liturgical vessels and other altar furnishings.[20] Not only did Suger write, "We profess that we must do homage also through the outward ornaments of sacred vessels..." but he explained, "Thus, when—out of my delight in the beauty of the house of God—the loveliness of the many-colored gems has called me away from external cares, and worthy meditation has induced me to reflect, transferring that which is material to that which is immaterial, on the diversity of the sacred virtues: then it seems to me that I see myself dwelling, as it were, in some strange region of the universe which neither exists entirely in the slime of the earth nor entirely in the purity of Heaven; and that, by the grace of God, I can be transported from this inferior to that higher world in an anagogical manner."[21]

Figure 33. Suger's Eagle Vase. Paris, Musée du Louvre

William D. Wixom
Chairman
Department of Medieval Art and The Cloisters
The Metropolitan Museum of Art

Notes

1. *De Administratione*, [XXXIV A], ed. Panofsky, 1979, 77.
2. De Montesquiou-Fezensac and Gaborit-Chopin, I, 1973, 3–59.
3. Conway, 1915.
4. *De Administratione*, XXXII, ed. Panofsky, 1979, 56–61; Verdier, 1970.
5. Lasko, 1972, 189; de Montesquiou-Fezensac and Gaborit-Chopin, I, 1973, 217–18, no. 195.
6. Swarzenski, 1958; Green, 1961; Lasko, 1972, 188–89.
7. *De Administratione*, XXXI, *De Consecratione*, V, ed. Panofsky, 1979, 54–57, 104–7.
8. De Montesquiou-Fezensac and Gaborit-Chopin, 1974.
9. De Montesquiou-Fezensac and Gaborit-Chopin, 1975.
10. Crosby, 1966, 23–28.
11. De Montesquiou-Fezensac and Gaborit-Chopin, III, 1977, pls. 22, 41–43, 47–48.
12. Heckscher, 1937, 210.
13. Heckscher, 1937, 212; von Simson, 1962, 50.
14. *De Administratione*, [XXXIV A], ed. Panofsky, 1979, 78–79; de Montesquiou-Fezensac and Gaborit-Chopin, III, 1977, pls. 23–24.
15. This banner was later conflated with the idea of the Oriflamme of Charlemagne; Spiegel, 1978, 30.
16. *De Consecratione*, II, ed. Panofsky, 1979, 86–89; Greenhill, 1976, 86–87.
17. *De Consecratione*, V, ed. Panofsky, 1979, 104–7.
18. Von Simson, 1962, 115, n. 73.
19. *De Administratione*, XXVII, ed. Panofsky, 1979, 46–49.
20. Von Simson, 1962, 119.
21. *De Administratione*, XXXIII, ed. Panofsky, 1979, 66–67, 62–65, respectively.

*23. Incense Boat ("Vase of Saint Éloi")

Green aventurine with flecks of mica
Byzantine(?), 6th–7th century(?)
Height, 5.8 cm. (2 5/16 in.); width, 8.5 cm. (3 3/8 in.);
length, 22.7 cm. (8 15/16 in.)
Paris, Bibliothèque Nationale, Cabinet des
Médailles, 374

Figure 34. Detail of Félibien's engraving (fig. 31)

Suger proudly chronicled the acquisition of this piece, which already had its metalwork mount with cloisonné settings for inset glass and stones (*De Administratione*, [XXXIV A]). This composite object had originally belonged to Louis VI, who pawned it. Redeemed by Suger, it was added by him to the series of altar utensils at the royal abbey. The goldsmith setting, destroyed at the beginning of the nineteenth century, was described in detail in the inventory of 1634 (de Montesquiou-Fezensac and Gaborit-Chopin, I, 1973, 165–66 no. 74) and is shown in Félibien's engraving of 1706 (fig. 34). The aventurine bowl was enlarged at the top by a quatrelobed upper rim in silver gilt, blue glass, emeralds, garnets, and pearls. This is the work that Suger attributed to Saint Éloi (d. 659). Since the descriptions suggest a possible similarity with Early Merovingian cloisonné objects such as the Merovingian or Burgundian oblong paten, dating from about 500, found near Gourdon (Saône-et-Loire) and now also in the Bibliothèque Nationale, it is reasonable to accept the attribution to the sixth or the seventh century proposed by de Montesquiou-Fezensac and Gaborit-Chopin (1977, 61). The aventurine bowl is thought to be a roughly contemporary Byzantine import.

Bibliography: Conway, 1915, 126–27, pl. IX, fig. 1; de Montesquiou-Fezensac and Gaborit-Chopin, I, 1973, 165–66 no. 74, III, 1977, 60–61 (bibl.), pl. 45B; Panofsky, 1979, 76–79.

106

23

24. The Crucifixion

Engraved rock crystal cabochon
Workshop of Charles the Bald
Mid-9th century
Height, 15.6 cm. (6⅛ in.); width, 10.5 cm. (4⅛ in.)
London, The British Museum, EG.561

Mentioned in the inventory of 1634 (de Montes-quiou-Fezensac and Gaborit-Chopin, I, 1973, 227 no. 200: 69, 288 no. 345), this large crystal once decorated Suger's tabernacle of Le Tombeau des Corps-Saints, the shrine for the relics of Saint Denis and his companions, Saints Rusticus and Eleutherius, which was destroyed in 1626–27. The exact identification is made possible by the correlation of the inventory citations and Félibien's engraving with an especially detailed description by Peiresc (de Montesquiou-Fezensac, 1954).

Engraved on its flat face are the Crucifixion, the mourning Virgin, and Saint John the Evangelist, and the personification of the sun and the moon, each holding a whip with three lashes. A serpent encircles the base of the cross. Attributed to one of the Carolingian ateliers of Charles the Bald (840–77), this important crystal was but one example among several adaptations of earlier carved gems by the workshop that was responsible for Suger's tabernacle (see page 102 above). While Suger does not mention this crystal, its appeal for him must have been considerable. Its size, luminosity, and completeness are impressive; its engraved imagery is refined yet expressive in its depiction of a key sacred subject: the culmination of Christ's Passion. Both symbolically and visually, this immense gem must have taken a primary position in the tabernacle, dominating the whole series of carved cameos and intaglios—most of them pagan—and precious jewels that Suger eagerly acquired from a variety of contemporary sources.

Bibliography: Crosby, 1972, 21, 84 n. 23, fig. 62B; Lasko, 1972, 61, 270 notes 6, 8; de Montesquiou-Fezensac and Gaborit-Chopin, I, 1973, 227 no. 200:69, 288 no. 345, III, 1977, 114–15 (bibl.), pl. 99.

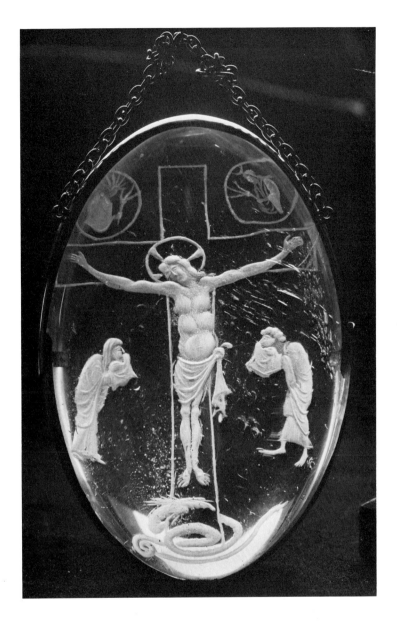

25 (detail)

25 (detail)

25. Chalice

Agate ("Sardonyx")
Egyptian, Alexandrian, 2nd century B.C.
Silver gilt, gold, filigree, cabochons, pearls, and glass
Saint-Denis, before 1147 and 19th century
Height, 19 cm. (7 ½ in.); diameter at base, 10.8 cm. (4 ¼ in.)
Washington, D.C., National Gallery of Art, Widener Collection, C–1

Suger does not mention the transformation of the ancient vessel that forms the core of this footed Chalice, but that he marveled at the beauty of the vessel is clear from his description:

> We also procured for the services at the aforesaid altar a precious chalice out of one solid sardonyx, which [word] derives from "sardius" and "onyx"; in which one [stone] the sard's red hue, by varying its property, so keenly vies with the blackness of the onyx that one property seems to be bent on trespassing upon the other.

De Administratione, [XXXIV A], ed. Panofsky, 1979, 79

The ancient vessel itself has been recently identified as Alexandrian, from the 2nd century B.C., by John D. Cooney (Panofsky, 1979, 221; Verdier, 1975, 700 n. 5).

The study of the post-Medieval changes in the Chalice must depend equally upon the recent unpublished technical studies conducted at the National Gallery of Art and upon a careful review of the entry in the inventory of 1634 (de Montesquiou-Fezensac and Gaborit-Chopin, I, 1973, 164–65 no. 71), the detailed watercolor drawing that Peiresc made in 1633 (fig. 35), and Félibien's engraving of 1706. Peiresc's illustration gives the clearest indication of the state of the Chalice before the changes of the eighteenth and nineteenth centuries. This watercolor shows that all of the gems were typically Medieval oval cabochons. A number of these have been replaced by faceted gems (Christensen, 1952). Many of the glass replacements are probably modern, including the white glass spheres that have been substituted for some of the pearls.

Originally, all five medallions on the foot depicted busts. Now only the gold repoussé bust of Christ remains. Peiresc's drawing is of the opposite side of the Chalice, showing clearly that the other busts represented the four Evangelists with the youthful Saint John the Evangelist near the center. These bust medallions were replaced after 1804 by the four medallions with Eucharistic symbols that we see today.

The probability that the lower part of the foot was much damaged would explain not only the replacement of four of the medallions but also the change in the lower edge of the foot, which, according to Peiresc, flared out beyond an imaginary plumb line suspended from the upper rim. This change caused a reduction in the total circumference of the lower edge and the elimination of the sequence of cabochons alternating with paired pearls depicted by Peiresc and similar to the sequence around the upper rim. The inscription, SUGER ABBAS, which was re-

25 (detail)

corded in 1739, had already disappeared when the Chalice was deposited in the Cabinet des Médailles in 1791, suggesting clearly the time frame for the damage to the foot.

Peiresc was presumably accurate in omitting a portion of the inward curls of the upper part of the handles. Since the extra curls of metal visible today appear in Félibien's engraving, we may be tempted to assume that they were elaborations of the eighteenth century. Certainly the simple curls on the handle of the Ewer support this (cat. no. 26). However, technical examination of the Chalice handles conducted under magnification may prove otherwise.

Suger's Chalice demonstrates a respect for Byzantine tradition. Its overall shape and proportion are generally similar to those of several Byzantine chalices made in the previous two centuries in Constantinople and brought back to Venice after the sack of Constantinople in 1204 (Wixom, 1967, 70; Hahnloser, 1971, nos. 41–43, 50). While these examples were not yet in western possession at the time that Suger's Chalice was completed, several similarities are compelling. The conical foot, originally graced with busts of holy personages and surmounted by a knob, the bowl of agate or sardonyx, the wide rim of silver gilt, and the handles that clamp the rim and knob tightly to the bowl are elements in the Suger Chalice that may be based in earlier Byzantine tradition. The one remaining medallion, that of Christ as Pantocrator, while clearly western in its modeling and in the paleographic character of the letter A (alpha), is nevertheless Byzantine in inspiration, as underscored by comparison with the repoussé medallions on the back cover of the Reliquary of the Archangel Michael, a Byzantine work of the first half of the eleventh century in the Treasury of San Marco (Hahnloser, 1971, no. 17, pl. XX).

The actual decorative detail of the Chalice, however, seems western in inspiration when compared with the metalwork of the late tenth and the eleventh centuries in the Rhineland. The filigree volutes of notched wire and the carefully positioned cabochons, alternating with smaller gems on the knob, or flanked by paired pearls on the upper and (lost) lower rims, seem to depend on the tradition represented by the first Cross of the Abbess Mathilde, c. 980, in Essen, and the Cross of the Abbess Theophanu, c. 1050, also in Essen (Swarzenski, 1954, fig. 69; Schnitzler, 1957, nos. 43, 46, pls. 143, 144, 155). The simplified leaf patterns engraved on the handles, a pervasive motif in manuscripts, especially recall similar patterns in the borders of Cologne manuscripts dating from 1050 to 1150 (Cologne, 1975, 155:c–15, 158:c–17, 159:c–15, 160:c–19, 233:g–2).

The question naturally arises as to where Suger's sardonyx fluted cup was mounted and transformed into a chalice with knobbed foot, and handles. Did Suger purchase a complete chalice or did he acquire only the sardonyx cup, seeing in it its future function as a chalice? Suger relates how he had the porphyry vase adapted into an eagle vase for the altar; he is silent about the transformation of the fluted cup. Of special importance in this context is the rock crystal vase given by Eleanor of Aquitaine to King Louis VII (then her husband) who in turn presented it to Suger for the abbey (fig. 36; de Montesquiou-Fezensac and Gaborit-Chopin, III, 1977, pls. 47, 48). Suger tells us that he had this vase "adorned with gems and gold" and inscribed (*De Administratione*, [XXXIV A], ed. Panofsky, 1979, 79). Since the filigree volutes of double-notched wire (Rosenberg, 1926, figs. 5, 6) and the employment of a sequence of cabochons alternating with pearls is so similar in both works, we may assume that the metalwork mounts and supports were made in the same workshop at the behest of Suger himself (de Montesquiou-Fezensac and Gaborit-Chopin, III, 1977, 58). The decoration of the neck and handle of the sardonyx Ewer shares in this community of details of technique and style. The three pieces have in common two principal characteristics. First, they are composite works with antique hard-stone vessels that have been transformed by metalwork settings into vessels for the altar (see pages 102–3 above). Second, they are closely related in the details and technique of this transformation. As a result, Suger's patronage for all three mountings seems conclusive.

The modern history of the Chalice is characterized by near tragedy, intrigue, mystery, and "discovery." After the French Revolution and the partial destruction of the treasures at Saint-Denis, the Chalice was deposited in the Cabinet des Médailles in the Bibliothèque Nationale in Paris. Stolen in 1804, together with several other items—some still lost—the Chalice was taken to England where it was purchased for the English antiquarian Charles Towneley (1737–1805), whose collection for the most part passed to The British Museum. The Chalice remained hidden from view, presumably in the possession of Towneley's heirs, until its sale to Harry Harding about 1920. Through the auspices of Jacob Goldschmidt and the Goldschmidt Galleries in New York, it was bought in 1922 by Joseph Widener for his distinguished collection at Elkins Park. Initially identified and studied in 1921 by Marc Rosenberg, whose publication did not appear until 1926, and subsequently "discovered" by Seymour de Ricci in 1923, the Chalice remained in the Widener Collection until that collection was given to the National Gallery of Art in Washington in 1942.

Ex collections: Bibliothèque Nationale, Cabinet des Médailles (Paris); Charles Towneley (England), 1805(?); Harry Harding (England), c. 1920; Goldschmidt Galleries (New York), until 1922; Joseph Widener (Elkins Park, Pa.), 1922–42.

Bibliography: Stoddard, 1966, 376–78, fig. 422; Wixom, 1967, 70, 71 (colorplate), 353–54 (bibl.); de Montesquiou-Fezensac and Gaborit-Chopin, I, 1973, 164–65 no. 71, III, 1977, 57–59 (bibl.), pls. 41–43; Brill, 1976.

see Cover

Figure 35. Suger's Chalice. Watercolor by Nicolas de Peiresc. Early seventeenth century. Paris, Bibliothèque Nationale

26. Ewer

Sardonyx
Byzantine, 5th or 11th century
Silver gilt, filigree, cabochons, and pearls
Saint-Denis, before 1147 and 15th century
Height, 35.7 cm. (14 1/16 in.)
Paris, Musée du Louvre, MR 127

Figure 36. Suger's Eleanor Vase. Paris, Musée du Louvre

In the words of Suger:

Further we added another vase shaped like a ewer, very similar to the former in material but not in form, whose little verses are these:

"Since we must offer libations to God with gems and gold,
I, Suger, offer this vase to the Lord."

De Administratione, [XXXIV A], ed. Panofsky, 1979, 79

A far more detailed reference, including the same inscription, may be found in the inventory of 1634 (de Montesquiou-Fezensac and Gaborit-Chopin, I, 1973, 150 no. 27).

Comparison with Byzantine vases in the San Marco Treasury and in the Louvre has led to the attribution of the sardonyx portion of Suger's Ewer, which is repeated tentatively here (de Montesquiou-Fezensac and Gaborit-Chopin, III, 1977, 41). The western twelfth-century metalwork includes the decorated neck of three cylinders, the compressed knob below the top cylinder, the three horizontal pearl- or cabochon-studded bands, the similarly decorated handle, the lid with a pomegranate-like knob, and the spout. Although the construction of the segmented neck with a compressed knob bordered with notched wire recalls the stems of several Byzantine chalices of the tenth and eleventh centuries (Hahnloser, 1971, 41, 49, 50), the bands with filigree volutes of double-notched wire and carefully spaced cabochons and pearls are so closely related in technique and configuration to the similar decoration on Suger's Chalice (cat. no. 25) and on the Eleanor Vase (fig. 36; de Montesquiou-Fezensac and Gaborit-Chopin, III, 1977, pls. 47–48) that a common Rhenish-influenced western workshop for all three pieces may be postulated. The portions of these objects that especially invite comparison are their encircling bands encrusted with spaced cabochons, paired pearls, and filigree of double-notched wire, seen on the upper rim of the Ewer, the upper and (lost) lower borders of the Chalice, and on the lower border of the Eleanor Vase. The jewel-encrusted and elegantly curved handle of the Ewer is a similar though more elongated version of the handles on the Chalice. The members of the workshop responsible for the goldsmiths' settings for Suger's three stone vessels must have been active at Saint-Denis, yet possibly may have come from Paris (de Montesquiou-Fezensac and Gaborit-Chopin, III, 1977, 42). Underscoring the indigenous aspect of some of Suger's projects is the occurrence of related motifs in stained glass, as previously noted (see page 67, and cat. nos. 16, 12).

The Ewer's present foot, with its embossments and inscription (which copies the original one), dates from the late fifteenth or early sixteenth century. This Late Medieval restoration indicates that severe damage or complete loss of the original foot had already occurred in the Middle Ages.

Bibliography: Steingräber, 1968, 23, 27, ill. 5; de Montesquiou-Fezensac and Gaborit-Chopin, I, 1973, 150 no. 27, III, 1977, 41–42 (bibl.), pl. 22.

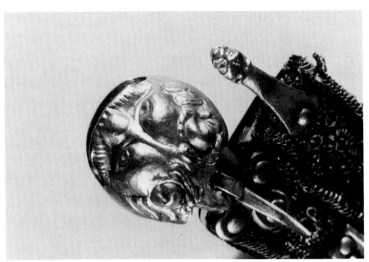

27 (detail)

27 (detail)

27. One of a Pair of Coronation Spurs

Gold, silver gilt, copper, garnets, and velvet
embroidered with spangles
Paris, 12th, 16th, and 19th centuries
Length, 17 cm. (6 11/16 in.); width, 8.5 cm. (3 3/8 in.)
Paris, Musée du Louvre, MS 86A

Described in the inventory of 1634 (de Montesquiou-Fezensac and Gaborit-Chopin, I, 1973, 184 no. 117), both spurs are recognized as composite objects with different dates for the various parts. Only the twelfth-century portions are of interest in the present context. These include the gold openwork plaques (several of which are unfinished) that decorate the outer faces of the arch of each spur, one of the lion masks on the later straps (the other mask is a copy), and both of the gold knobs. Without any reference in Suger's writings, it is impossible to propose a precise date in the twelfth century for this work. However, the biting serpentine and foliate motifs may be viewed as metalwork counterparts of a few of the decorative details on the facade columns (cat. no. 2B). The undulating yet symmetrical character of the metalwork plaques invites comparison with some of the stained-glass borders from Saint-Denis (cat. no. 18).

Traditionally, the coronation of the kings of France occurred at Rheims, but the custody of the coronation regalia was the province of the Abbey of Saint-Denis (Doublet, 1625, 366; Conway, 1915, 145; de Montesquiou-Fezensac and Gaborit-Chopin, III, 1977, pls. 6, 64–75, 94, 105). The origin of this tradition in Merovingian times was immeasurably strengthened by Suger (see pages 103–4). Nevertheless, the role of the twelfth-century portions of the spurs is uncertain.

Bibliography: de Montesquiou-Fezensac and Gaborit-Chopin, I, 1973, 184 no. 117, III, 1977, 81–82 (bibl.), pl. 74.

27

28. Two of Three Plaques, from a Portable Altar

Ivory

France, Saint-Denis, 1st half(?) of the 12th century

A. Height, 4.6 cm. (1 13/16 in.); length, 10.3 cm. (4 1/16 in.)

B. Height, 4.6 cm. (1 13/16 in.); length, 14.3 cm. (5 5/8 in.)

Paris, Musée du Louvre, OA 2008–2010

28B (detail)

These openwork plaques from a portable altar cannot be identified in any of the inventories or illustrative records of the treasury of Saint-Denis. Their history prior to acquisition in 1864 by the Louvre is unknown. The two longer plaques with a series of disputing apostles, each identified by inscriptions in the arcades above, were undoubtedly the long sides of a portable altar. The plaque with the nimbed Saint Denis and Saints Rusticus and Eleutherius, each with identifying inscriptions, was one of the altar's short ends. The reliefs may have been mounted against a contrasting material such as gilt metal and framed at the top and bottom by angled borders that may have continued the motifs of the foliate borders at the ends of the arcades.

The iconography of the end plaque is one of the compelling reasons for attributing the plaques to a workshop closely associated with the Abbey of Saint-Denis during Suger's time (Goldschmidt, 1926, 20). In subject and format the two longer plaques are obviously related to the Apostles Relief as well (cat. no. 6). Stylistic and decorative correspondences with this and other sculptures and with stained glass, despite the differences in scale and materials, also support this attribution. The foliate rinceaux on the short plaque have parallels in the stained glass (cat. no. 16) and in one of the colonnettes for the facade (cat. no. 2B). The pearled borders also may be seen in some of the stained-glass borders (cat. no. 15). The use of masks, contorted animals, and birds as decorative motifs finds an echo in the colonnettes (cat. no. 2B). The mask between the central arcades of the long plaque may be seen similarly imbedded in the corner of the unfinished end of the Apostles Relief (cat. no. 6; Crosby, 1972, pl. 51). Most important, the drapery style of the ivory apostles is closely related to the much larger figures of the apostles to the right of Christ in the Last Judgment tympanum of the central portal of the west facade (Crosby and Blum, 1973, pl. VIb).

The carver of the plaques has been described as Mosan, a possibility that is supported by a comparison of the plaques with Mosan ivories of 1100 to 1120 in which there are similar physiognomic types, gestures, damp-fold and strand-like draperies, and beaded and foliate borders (Cologne, 1972, I, 287–88, J–12, J–14). However, because of the iconography and the stylistic association with the sculptures and stained glass at the abbey, the attribution of the plaques to a French carver inspired by Mosan art is preferred (Grodecki, 1947, 62; Gaborit-Chopin, 1978, 112, 200).

Bibliography: Crosby, 1972, 62–63, 64–65, 95 n. 30, fig. 67; de Montesquiou-Fezensac and Gaborit-Chopin, III, 1977, 132–33, pl. 113; Gaborit-Chopin, 1978, 112, 200 (bibl.), fig. 160.

28A

28B

117

Bibliography

Works cited in the catalogue:

ALEXANDER, 1970
Alexander, J[onathan] J[ames] G[raham], *Norman Illumination at Mont St Michel, 966–1100*, Oxford, 1970.

Amsterdam, 1973, Rijksmuseum, *Vitraux...*, see GRODECKI and PERROT, 1973

AUBERT, 1945
Aubert, Marcel, "Têtes de statues-colonnes du portail occidental de Saint-Denis," *Bulletin monumental*, LIII, 1945, 243–48.

AUBERT and BEAULIEU, 1950
Aubert, Marcel, and Beaulieu, Michèle, *Musée National du Louvre: Description raisonnée des sculptures du Moyen Âge, de la Renaissance et des temps modernes, I: Moyen Âge*, Paris, 1950.

BAUCH, 1976
Bauch, Kurt, *Das mittelalterliche Grabbild*, Berlin, 1976.

BEYER and GRODECKI, 1965
Beyer, Victor, and Grodecki, Louis, *Mille Ans d'art du vitrail* (exh. cat.), 2 vols., Strasbourg, Musée de l'Ancienne Douane, 1965.

BLUM, 1978
Blum, Pamela Z., "An Archaeological Analysis of the Statue-Column from Saint-Maur-des-Fossés at Dumbarton Oaks," *Gesta*, XVII/2, 1978, 23–28.

BRECK, 1913
Breck, Joseph, "Recent Accessions, XII Century," *Bulletin of The Metropolitan Museum of Art*, VIII, 11, November 1913, 249–50.

BRECK, 1921
Breck, Joseph, "A King of Judah and Other Mediaeval Sculptures," *Bulletin of The Metropolitan Museum of Art*, XVI, 3, March 1921, 48–52.

BRILL, 1976
Brill, Robert H., *Report on the Microscopic Examination of the Suger Chalice*, Corning, New York, 1976, unpublished study.

BROUILLETTE, 1977
Brouillette, Diane, *Senlis: Un Moment de la sculpture gothique* (exh. cat.), Senlis, Hôtel de Vermandois, 1977.

CAHIER and MARTIN, 1841–44
Cahier, Charles, and Martin, Arthur, *Monographie de la cathédrale de Bourges, I: Vitraux du XIIIᵉ siècle*, Paris, 1841–44.

CAHN, 1977
Cahn, Walter, "Romanesque Sculpture in American Collections, XVI: The Academy of the New Church, Bryn Athyn, Pa.," *Gesta*, XVI/2, 1977, 69–79.

CAHN and SEIDEL, 1979
Cahn, Walter, and Seidel, Linda, *Romanesque Sculpture in American Collections, I: New England Museums*, New York, 1979.

CARTELLIERI, 1898
Cartellieri, Otto, *Abt Suger von Saint-Denis*, Berlin, 1898.

CHRISTENSEN, 1952
Christensen, Erwin O., *Objects of Medieval Art from the Widener Collection*, Washington, D.C., 1952.

Cleveland, 1967, The Cleveland Museum of Art, *Treasures...*, see WIXOM, 1967

COLOGNE, 1972
Rhein und Maas: Kunst und Kultur 800–1400 (exh. cat.), 2 vols., Cologne, Schnütgen-Museum, 1972.

COLOGNE, 1975
Monumenta Annonis: Köln und Siegburg, Weltbild und Kunst im hohen Mittelalter (exh. cat.), Anton Legner, ed., Cologne, Schnütgen-Museum, 1975.

CONWAY, 1915
Conway, William Martin, "The Abbey of Saint-Denis and Its Ancient Treasures," *Archaeologia or Miscellaneous Tracts Relating to Antiquity*, LXVI, 2nd series, XVI, 1915, 103–58.

COTHREN, 1978
Cothren, Michael, "A Re-evaluation of the Iconography and Design of the Infancy Window from the Abbey of Saint-Denis," *Gesta*, XVII/1, 1978, 74–75.

CROSBY, 1942
Crosby, Sumner McKnight, *The Abbey of Saint-Denis*, I, New Haven, 1942.

CROSBY, 1947
Crosby, Sumner McKnight, "Fouilles exécutées récemment dans la Basilique de Saint-Denis," *Bulletin monumental*, CV, 1947, 167–87.

CROSBY, 1950
Crosby, Sumner McKnight, "Séance du 9 juillet 1947," *Bulletin de la Société nationale des Antiquaires de France*, 1945–47, 253–56.

CROSBY, 1953
Crosby, Sumner McKnight, *L'Abbaye royale de Saint-Denis*, Paris, 1953.

CROSBY, 1966
Crosby, Sumner McKnight, "An International Workshop in the Twelfth Century," *Journal of World History*, X, 1, 1966, 19–30.

CROSBY, 1969
Crosby, Sumner McKnight, "A Relief from Saint-Denis in a Paris Apartment," *Gesta*, VIII/2, 1969, 45–46.

CROSBY, 1970
Crosby, Sumner McKnight, "The West Portals of Saint-Denis and the Saint-Denis Style," *Gesta*, IX/2, 1970, 1–11.

CROSBY, 1972
Crosby, Sumner McKnight, *The Apostle Bas-Relief at Saint-Denis* (Yale Publications in the History of Art, XXI), New Haven and London, 1972.

CROSBY, 1980
Crosby, Sumner McKnight, "Abbot Suger's Program for His New Abbey Church," paper read at the Monasticism and the Arts Symposium, Spring 1980, at Yale University, New Haven, forthcoming.

CROSBY and BLUM, 1973
Crosby, Sumner McKnight, and Blum, Pamela Z., "Le Portail central de la façade occidentale de Saint-Denis," *Bulletin monumental*, 131–III, 1973, 209–66.

DELAPORTE and HOUVET, 1926
Delaporte, Yves, and Houvet, Étienne, *Les Vitraux de la cathédrale de Chartres*, 4 vols., Chartres, 1926.

DODWELL, 1971
Dodwell, Charles Reginald, *Painting in Europe: 800 to 1200*, Harmondsworth, England, 1971.

DOUBLET, 1625
Doublet, Dom Jacques, *Histoire de l'abbaye de Saint-Denys en France....*, 2 vols., Paris, 1625.

FÉLIBIEN, 1706
Félibien, Dom Michel, *Histoire de l'abbaye royale de Saint-Denys en France*, Paris, 1706.

FORMIGÉ, 1960
Formigé, Jules, *L'Abbaye royale de Saint-Denis: Recherches nouvelles*, Paris, 1960.

FRANKL, 1960
Frankl, Paul, *The Gothic: Literary Sources and Interpretations through Eight Centuries*, Princeton, 1960.

GABORIT-CHOPIN, 1978
Gaborit-Chopin, Danielle, *Ivoires du Moyen âge*, Fribourg, 1978.

LE GENTIL DE LA GALASIÈRE, 1791
Le Gentil de la Galasière, "Observations sur plusiers monumens gothiques...sur lesquels sont gravés les signes du zodiaque et quelques hyérogliphes égyptiens relatifs à la religion d'Isis," *Histoire de l'académie royal des sciences*, XC, Paris, 1788, 390–438.

GERSON, 1970
Gerson, Paula, "The West Facade of St.-Denis: An Iconographic Study," Ph.D. dissertation, New York, Columbia University, 1970, microfilm.

GOLDSCHMIDT, 1926
Goldschmidt, Adolf, *Die Elfenbeinskulpturen aus der romanischen Zeit, XI–XIII Jahrhundert*, IV, Berlin, 1926.

GÓMEZ-MORENO, 1968
Gómez-Moreno, Carmen, *Medieval Art from Private Collections* (exh. cat.), New York, The Metropolitan Museum of Art (The Cloisters), 1968.

GREEN, 1961
Green, Rosalie, "Ex Ungue Leonem," *Essays in Honor of Erwin Panofsky*, New York, 1961, 157–69.

GREENHILL, 1976
Greenhill, Eleanor S. "Eleanor, Abbot Suger and Saint-Denis," *Eleanor of Aquitaine: Patron and Politician*, William W. Kibler, ed., Austin and London, 1976, 81–113.

GRODECKI, 1947
Grodecki, Louis, *Ivoires français: arts, styles et techniques*, Paris, 1947.

GRODECKI, 1952
Grodecki, Louis, "Fragments de vitraux provenant de St.-Denis," *Bulletin monumental*, CX, 1952–1, 51–62.

GRODECKI, 1953
Grodecki, Louis, *Vitraux de France du XIᵉ au XVIᵉ siècle* (exh. cat.), Paris, Musée des Arts Décoratifs, 1953.

GRODECKI, 1958
Grodecki, Louis, "Une Scène de la vie de St. Benoît provenant de Saint-Denis au Musée de Cluny," *La Revue des arts*, VIII, 1958, 161–71.

GRODECKI, 1959
Grodecki, Louis, "La 'Première Sculpture gothique.' Wilhelm Vöge et l'état actuel des problèmes," *Bulletin monumental*, CXVII, 1959–4, 265–89.

GRODECKI, 1961
Grodecki, Louis, "Vitraux allégoriques de St.-Denis," *Art de France*, I, 1961, 19–46.

GRODECKI, *ARTIBUS*, 1961
Grodecki, Louis, "Les Vitraux de Saint-Denis. L'Enfance du Christ," *De Artibus Opuscula XL. Essays in Honor of Erwin Panofsky*, Millard Meiss, ed., New York, 1961, 170–86.

GRODECKI, 1976
Grodecki, Louis, *Les Vitraux de Saint-Denis, I: Histoire et restitution (Corpus Vitrearum Medii Aevi*, France "Études" I), Paris, 1976.

GRODECKI, 1977
Grodecki, Louis, with the collaboration of Catherine Brisac and Claudine Lautier, *Le Vitrail roman*, Fribourg, 1977.

GRODECKI and PERROT, 1973
Grodecki, Louis, and Perrot, Françoise, *Vitraux de France* (exh. cat.), Amsterdam, Rijksmuseum, 1973.

GUILHERMY, 1844
Guilhermy, Baron François de, *Détails historiques. Saint-Denis*, 1840–72.

HAHNLOSER, 1971
Hahnloser, Hans, *Il Tesoro di San Marco, II: Il tesoro e il museo*, Florence, 1971.

HECKSCHER, 1937
Heckscher, W[illiam] S[ebastian], "Relics of Pagan Antiquity in Mediaeval Settings," *Journal of the Warburg Institute*, 1, 1937, 204–20.

HOFFMANN, 1968
Hoffmann, Konrad, "Sugers 'Anagogisches Fenster' in St. Denis," *Wallraf-Richartz-Jahrbuch*, XXX, 1968, 57–88.

KATZENELLENBOGEN, 1959
Katzenellenbogen, Adolf, *The Sculptural Programs of Chartres Cathedral: Christ–Mary–Ecclesia*, Baltimore, 1959.

KERBER, 1966
Kerber, Bernhard, *Burgund und die Entwicklung der französischen Kathedralskulptur im zwölften Jahrhundert*, Recklinghausen, 1966.

LASKO, 1972
Lasko, Peter, *Ars Sacra: 800–1200*, Harmondsworth, England, 1972.

DE LASTEYRIE, 1857
de Lasteyrie, Ferdinand, *Histoire de la peinture sur verre d'après ses monuments en France*, 2 vols., Paris, 1857.

LEBEUF, 1754
Lebeuf, Abbé Jean, *Histoire de la ville et tout le diocèse de Paris, III: Histoire de banlieue ecclésiastique de Paris*, Paris, 1754.

LECOY DE LA MARCHE, 1867
Lecoy de la Marche, A[lbert], ed., *Oeuvres complètes de Suger*, Paris, 1867.

LENOIR, 1818
Lenoir, Alexandre Albert, *Atlas des monuments des arts libéraux, mécaniques et industriels de la France, depuis les Gaulois jusqu'au règne de François Iᵉʳ*, Paris, 1818.

LENOIR, 1856
Lenoir, Alexandre Albert, *Traité de la peinture sur verre et description de vitraux anciens et modernes*, Paris, 1856.

LILLE, 1978
Sculptures romanes et gothiques du nord de la France (exh. cat.), Lille, Musée des Beaux-Arts, 1978.

LYONS, 1894
Catalogue du Musée des Beaux-Arts de la Ville de Lyon, Lyons, 1894.

MABILLON, 1668–1701
Mabillon, Jean, ed., *Acta Sanctorum Ordinis Sancti Benedicti*, 9 vols., Lyons–Paris, 1668–1701.

MÂLE, 1978
Mâle, Émile, *Religious Art in France, the Twelfth Century*, Paris, 1922; 2nd ed., Harry Bober, ed., Marthiel Mathews, trans., Princeton, 1978.

MILLET, 1638
Millet, Dom Germain, *Le Trésor sacré ou inventaire des saintes reliques et autres précieux joyaux du trésor de l'abbaye royale de Saint-Denys en France*, 2nd ed., Paris, 1638.

DE MONTESQUIOU-FEZENSAC, 1954
de Montesquiou-Fezensac, Blaise, "A Carolingian Rock Crystal from the Abbey of Saint-Denis at the British Museum," *The Antiquaries Journal*, XXXIV, 1–2, January–April 1954, 38–43.

DE MONTESQUIOU-FEZENSAC and GABORIT-CHOPIN, 1973–77
de Montesquiou-Fezensac, Blaise, and Gaborit-Chopin, Danielle, *Le Trésor de Saint-Denis*, 3 vols., Paris, 1973–77.

DE MONTESQUIOU-FEZENSAC and GABORIT-CHOPIN, 1974
de Montesquiou-Fezensac, Blaise, and Gaborit-Chopin, Danielle, "Le 'Tombeau des corps-saints' à l'abbaye de Saint-Denis," *Cahiers archéologiques*, XXIII, 1974, 81–94.

DE MONTESQUIOU-FEZENSAC and GABORIT-CHOPIN, 1975
de Montesquiou-Fezensac, Blaise, and Gaborit-Chopin, Danielle, "Camées et intailles du trésor de St.-Denis," *Cahiers archéologiques*, XXIV, 1975, 137–62.

MONTFAUCON, 1729
Montfaucon, Dom Bernard de, *Les monumens de la monarchie françoise qui comprennent l'histoire de France avec les figures de chaque règne que l'injure des tems a épargnées*, 5 vols., Paris, 1729–39.

New York, 1968, The Metropolitan Museum of Art (The Cloisters), *Medieval Art ...*, see GÓMEZ-MORENO, 1968

NORDENFALK and GRABAR, 1958
Nordenfalk, Carl, and Grabar, André, *Early Medieval Painting from the Fourth to the Eleventh Century*, New York, 1958.

OSTOIA, 1955
Ostoia, Vera K., "A Statue from Saint-Denis," *Bulletin of The Metropolitan Museum of Art*, XIII, 10, June 1955, 298–304.

PANOFSKY, 1979
Panofsky, Erwin, ed. and trans., *Abbot Suger on the Abbey Church of St. Denis and Its Art Treasures*, Princeton, 1946; 2nd ed., Gerda Panofsky-Soergel, ed., Princeton, 1979.

Paris, 1953, Musée des Arts Décoratifs, *Vitraux...*, see GRODECKI, 1953

PARIS, 1968
L'Europe gothique, XIIᵉ–XIVᵉ siècles (exh. cat.), Paris, Musée National du Louvre (Council of Europe), 1968.

Perrot, Françoise, see GRODECKI and PERROT, 1973

PLANCHER, 1739
Plancher, Dom Urbain, *Histoire générale et particulière de Bourgogne*, I, Dijon, 1739.

PORCHER, 1959
Porcher, Jean, *Medieval French Miniatures*, New York, 1959.

PORTER, 1923
Porter, Arthur Kingsley, *The Romanesque Sculpture of the Pilgrimage Roads*, 10 vols., Boston, 1923.

PRESSOUYRE, 1967
Pressouyre, Léon, "Une Tête du Louvre prétendue diony-
sienne," *Bulletin de la Société nationale des Antiquaires de France*, 1967, 242–50.

PRESSOUYRE, 1970
Pressouyre, Léon, Review of "La Renaissance du XIIᵉ siècle," *Revue de l'art*, 7, 1970, 98–100.

PRESSOUYRE, 1973
Pressouyre, Léon, "St. Bernard to St. Francis: Monastic Ideals and Iconographic Programs in the Cloister," *Gesta*, XII, 1973, 71–92.

PRESSOUYRE, 1976
Pressouyre, Léon, "Une Tête de reine du portail central de Saint-Denis," *Gesta*, XV, 1976, 151–60.

Providence, 1969, Museum of Art, Rhode Island School of Design, see SCHER, 1969

QUARRÉ, 1957
Quarré, Pierre, "La Sculpture des anciens portails de Saint-Bénigne de Dijon," *Gazette des Beaux-Arts*, 6th series, L, October 1957, 177–94.

QUARRÉ, 1962
Quarré, Pierre, "L'Abbé Lebeuf et l'interprétation du portail de Saint-Bénigne de Dijon," *L'Abbé Lebeuf et le Jansenisme: XIIᵉᵐᵉ Congrès de l'Association bourguignonne des Sociétés savantes*, Auxerre, 1962, 281–87.

ROSENBERG, 1926
Rosenberg, Marc, "Ein wiedergefundener Kelch," *Festschrift zum sechszigsten Geburtstag von Paul Clemen*, Bonn, 1926.

ROSS, 1940
Ross, Marvin Chauncey, "Monumental Sculptures from St.-Denis: An Identification of Fragments from the Portal," *The Journal of the Walters Art Gallery*, III, 1940, 91–107.

SAUERLÄNDER, 1962
Sauerländer, Willibald, "Skulpturen des 12. Jahrhunderts in Châlons-sur-Marne," *Zeitschrift für Kunstgeschichte*, 25, 1962, 97–123.

SAUERLÄNDER, 1970
Sauerländer, Willibald, "Sculpture on Early Gothic Churches: The State of Research and Open Questions," *Gesta*, IX/2, 1970, 32–48.

SAUERLÄNDER, 1972
Sauerländer, Willibald, *Gothic Sculpture in France 1140–1270*, New York, 1972.

SAUERLÄNDER, 1974
Sauerländer, Willibald, Review of Sumner McKnight Crosby, *The Apostle Bas-Relief at Saint-Denis*, *The Art Bulletin*, LVI, 3, 1974, 438–39.

SCHER, 1969
Scher, Stephen K., *The Renaissance of the Twelfth Century* (exh. cat.), Providence, Museum of Art, Rhode Island School of Design, 1969.

SCHLINK, 1970
Schlink, Wilhelm, *Zwischen Cluny und Clairvaux*, Berlin, 1970.

SCHNITZLER, 1957
Schnitzler, Hermann, *Rheinische Schatzkammer*, I, Düsseldorf, 1957.

Seidel, Linda, see CAHN and SEIDEL, 1979

Senlis, 1977, Hôtel de Vermandois, *Senlis...*, see BROUILLETTE, 1977

VON SIMSON, 1956, see below

VON SIMSON, 1962
von Simson, Otto, *The Gothic Cathedral. The Origins of Gothic Architecture and the Medieval Concept of Order*, London and New York, 1956; rev. ed., New York, 1962.

121

SPIEGEL, 1978
Spiegel, Gabrielle M., *The Chronicle Tradition of Saint-Denis: A Survey* (Medieval Classics: Texts and Studies, X), Brookline, Mass., 1978.

STEINGRÄBER, 1968
Steingräber, Erich, ed., *Royal Treasures*, New York, 1968.

STODDARD, 1952
Stoddard, Whitney S., *The West Portals of Saint-Denis and Chartres: Sculpture in the Île-de-France from 1140 to 1190, Theory of Origins*, Cambridge, Mass., 1952.

STODDARD, 1966
Stoddard, Whitney S., *Monastery and Cathedral in France; Medieval Architecture, Sculpture, Stained Glass, Manuscripts, the Art of the Church Treasuries*, Middletown, Conn., 1966

STODDARD, 1973
Stoddard, Whitney S., *The Façade of Saint-Gilles-du-Gard: Its Influence on French Sculpture*, Middletown, Conn., 1973.

Strasbourg, 1965, Musée de l'Ancienne Douane, *Mille Ans...*, see BEYER and GRODECKI, 1965

Suger, *Oeuvres complètes...*, see LECOY DE LA MARCHE, 1867

SWARZENSKI, 1954
Swarzenski, Hanns, *Monuments of Romanesque Art*, London, 1954.

SWARZENSKI, 1958
Swarzenski, Hanns, "The Song of the Three Worthies," *Bulletin of the Museum of Fine Arts, Boston*, LVI, 303, Spring 1958, 30–49.

THÉREL, 1963
Thérel, Marie-Louise, "Comment la patrologie peut éclairer l'archéologie: À propos de l'Arbre de Jessé et des statues-colonnes de Saint-Denis," *Cahiers de civilisation médiévale Xᵉ–XIIᵉ siècles*, VI, 2, April–June 1963, 145–58.

VAN MARLE, 1921
Van Marle, Raimond, "Twelfth Century French Sculpture in America," *Art in America*, X, 1, December 1921, 3–16.

VERDIER, 1975
Verdier, Philippe, "Réflexions sur l'esthétique de Suger...," *Mélanges offerts à E.-R. Labande*, Paris, 1975, 699–709.

VÖGE, 1894
Vöge, Wilhelm, *Die Anfänge des monumentalen Stiles im Mittelalter. Eine Untersuchung über die erste Blütezeit französischer Plastik*, Strassburg, 1894.

WATSON, 1934
Watson, Arthur, *The Early Iconography of the Tree of Jesse*, Oxford, 1934.

WELLS, 1965
Wells, William, *Stained and Painted Glass: Burrell Collection*, Glasgow, 1965.

WIXOM, 1967
Wixom, William D., *Treasures from Medieval France* (exh. cat.), The Cleveland Museum of Art, 1967.

WULF, 1979
Wulf, Walter, *Die Kapitellplastik des Sugerbaus von Saint-Denis*, Frankfurt-am-Main, 1979.

ZARNECKI, 1979
Zarnecki, George, *Romanesque Sculpture at Lincoln Cathedral*, Lincoln Minster Pamphlets, 1970; reprinted in *idem, Studies in Romanesque Sculpture*, London, 1979, chap. XVI–25.

Selected works not cited in the catalogue:

Aachen, 1965, *Die Ausstellung Karl der Grosse: Werk und Wirkung* (exh. cat.), Rathaus (Council of Europe).

Adler, Alfred, "Pèlerinage de Charlemagne in a new light on Saint-Denis," *Speculum*, 22, 550–61.

Aubert, Marcel, and others, *Le Vitrail français*, Paris, 1958.

Ayzac, Félicie de, *Histoire de l'abbaye de Saint-Denis*, Paris, 1860–61.

Babelon, Ernest, *Histoire de la gravure sur gemmes en France depuis les origines jusqu'à l'époque contemporaine*, Paris, 1902.

———, *Le Cabinet des médailles et antiques de la Bibliothèque nationale. Notice historique et guide du visiteur, I: Les Antiques et les objets d'art*, Paris, 1924.

Barbet de Jouy, Henri, *Notice des antiquités, objets du Moyen Âge, de la Renaissance et des temps modernes composant le Musée des Souverains*, Paris, 1866.

Baum, Julius, "Karolingische geschnittene Bergkristalle," *Frühmittelalterliche Kunst in den Alpenländern*, Olten and Lausanne, Switzerland, 1954.

Bégule, Lucien, *Vitraux du moyen-âge et de la renaissance dans la région lyonnaise*, Paris, 1911.

Blum, Pamela Z. "The Saint Benedict Cycle on the Capitals of the Crypt at Saint-Denis," *Gesta*, XX/1, 1981, 73–88.

Branner, Robert, *Chartres Cathedral*, New York, 1969.

Chabouillet, Anatole, *Catalogue général et raisonné des camées et pierres gravées de la Bibliothèque impériale suivi de la description des autres monuments exposés dans le Cabinet des Médailles et Antiques*, Paris, 1858.

Clark, William W., "Spatial Innovations in the Chevet of Saint-Germain-des-Prés," *Journal of the Society of Architectural Historians*, XXXVIII, 4, December 1979, 348–65, and addendum.

Crosby, Sumner McKnight, "The Abbey of St.-Denis in the XII Century," Ph.D. dissertation, New Haven, Yale University, 1937, unpublished.

———, "Early Gothic Architecture: New Problems as a Result of the St. Denis Excavations," *Journal of the Society of Architectural Historians*, VII, 3–4, July–December 1948, 13–16.

———, "Excavations in the Abbey Church of St.-Denis, 1948. The Façade of Fulrad's Church," *Proceedings of the American Philosophical Society*, XCIII, 1949, 347 seq.

———, "Abbot Suger's St.-Denis. The New Gothic," *Studies in Western Art; Acts of the Twentieth International Congress of the History of Art*, I, Princeton, 1963, 85–91.

———, "The Inside of St.-Denis' West Façade," *Gedenkschrift Ernst Gall*, Margaret Kühn and Louis Grodecki, eds., Berlin and Munich, 1965, 59–68.

———, "Crypt and Choir Plans at Saint-Denis," *Gesta*, 5, 1966, 4–8.

———, "Masons' Marks at Saint-Denis," *Mélanges offerts à René Crozet*, II, Poitiers, 1966, 711–17.

———, "Sous le Dallage de l'abbaye royale de Saint-Denis," *Archeologia*, 1967, 14, January–February, 34–38; 15, March–April, 71–75.

———, "Excavations at Saint-Denis—July 1967," *Gesta*, VII, 1968, 48–50.

———, "The Plan of the Western Bays of Suger's New Church at St.-Denis," *Journal of the Society of Architectural Historians*, XXVII, 1, March 1968, 39–43.

Crown, Carol V., "The Winchester Psalter and 'l'Enfance du Christ' Window at St.-Denis," *The Burlington Magazine*, February 1975, 79–83.

Dalton, O[rmonde] M[addick], *Catalogue of the engraved gems in the British Museum, Post-Classical Periods*, London, 1915.

Debret, François, "Notice sur les diverses constructions et restaurations de l'église de St.-Denis," *Séance publique des cinq Académies*, 1842, 9–28.

Delbrück, Richard, *Antike Porphyrwerke*, Berlin and Leipzig, 1932.

Drury, William D., *A Guide to Wilton Parish Church and the Old Church of St. Mary's*, Wilton, England, 1959.

Erlande-Brandenburg, Alain, *L'Église abbatiale de Saint-Denis, I: Historique et Visite*, Paris, 1976.

Evans, Joan, "Die Adlervase des Sugerius," *Pantheon*, X, July–December 1932, 221–23.

———, *Life in Medieval France*, New York, 1957.

Friend, A[lbert] M[athias], "Carolingian Art in the Abbey of St.-Denis, *Art Studies*, I, 1923, 67–75.

Gaborit-Chopin, Danielle, "Le Croix de l'abbé Suger," *Bulletin monumental*, 128–III, 1970, 243–47.

Gabrielli, Noemi, "Vetrata romanica nel Museo Civico di Torino," *Torino*, March 1932, 28–32.

Gauthier, Marie-Madeleine, "Mélanges: le trésor de Saint-Denis—Inventaire de 1634," *Cahiers de civilisation médiévale*, XVIII, 2, 1975, 149–56.

Gerson, Paula, "The Lintels of the West Façade of Saint-Denis," *Journal of the Society of Architectural Historians*, XXXIV, 3, 1975, 189–97.

Gilbert, Antoine Pierre Marie, *Description historique de l'église royale de Saint-Denis*, Paris, 1815.

Grodecki, Louis, *The Stained Glass of French Churches*, Rosemary Edmunds and A. D. B. Sylvester, trans., London, 1948.

———, "Vitrail et architecture aux XIIᵉ et XIIIᵉ siècles," *Gazette des Beaux-Arts*, II, 1949, 6–21.

———, "L'Abbaye de Saint-Denis-en-France," *Critique*, no. 75–76, August–September 1953, 723–34.

———, "Vidrieras Romanicas," *Goya*, 43–45, 1961, 120–27.

———, "Vitraux de Saint-Denis au Château de Highcliffe," *Bulletin de la Société nationale des Antiquaires de France*, 1972, 104–7.

———; Mütherich, Florentine; Taralon, Jean; and Wormald, Francis, *Le Siècle de l'An Mil*, Paris, 1973.

Guibert, Joseph, *Les Dessins du Cabinet Peiresc au Cabinet des estampes de la Bibliothèque nationale, antiquités moyen-âge, Renaissance*, Paris, 1910.

Guilhermy, Baron François de, "Restauration de l'église royale de Saint-Denis," *Annales archéologiques*, V, 1846, 212–14.

———, *Monographie de l'église royale de Saint-Denis: Tombeaux et figures historiques*, Paris, 1848.

———, *Inscriptions de la France du Vᵉ siècle au XVIIIᵉ: ancien diocèse de Paris* (collection de documents inédits sur l'histoire de France), 5 vols., Paris, 1873–83.

Héliot, Pierre, "La Diversité de l'architecture gothique à ses débuts en France," *Gazette des Beaux-Arts*, 6th series, LXIX, 1967, 269–306.

Hoffmann, Konrad, *The Year 1200* (exh. cat.), I, New York, The Metropolitan Museum of Art, 1970.

Huard, Georges, "Percier et l'abbaye de St.-Denis," *Les Monuments historiques de la France*, I, 1936, 134–44, 173–82.

Hubert, J[ean]; Porcher, J[ean]; and Volbach, W[olfgang] F[riedrich], *L'Empire carolingien*, Paris, 1968.

Hugo, Abel, *Les Tombeaux de Saint-Denis, ou description historique de cette abbaye...*, Paris, 1825.

Ingelheim am Rhein (774–1974) Geschichte und Gegenwart (exh. cat.), François Lachenal, ed., Ingelheim, Germany, 1974.

Jaquemet, Chanoine Jules, *Église de Saint-Denis, sa crypte, ses tombeaux, ses chapelles, son trésor*, Paris, 1867.

Kirby, H. T., "Ancient Glass at Twycross," *The Burlington Magazine for Connoisseurs*, lxxxii, 480, May 1943, 124–27.

Labarte, Jules, *Histoire des arts industriels au Moyen âge et à l'époque de la Renaissance*, 6 vols., Paris, 1864–66.

Lacroix, Paul, ed., "Récolements et état descriptif du trésor de St.-Denis établi le...15 frimaire an II [5 décembre 1793]," *Revue universelle des arts*, IV.

Lafond, Jean, *Pratique de la peinture sur verre à l'usage des curieux, suivie d'un essai historique sur le jaune d'argent et d'une note sur les plus anciens verres gravés*, Rouen, 1943.

———, "Les Vitraux français en Angleterre: Wilton, XIIᵉ et XIIIᵉ siècles," *Bulletin de la Société nationale des Antiquaires de France*, 1959, 241–43.

Lamm, Carl Johan, *Mittelalterliches Gläser und Steinschnittarbeiten aus den nahen Osten*, 2 vols., Berlin, 1930.

Levavasseur, Chanoine F., *La Basilique de Saint-Denys: Guide du Visiteur*, 3rd ed., Paris, 1965.

Lombard-Jourdan, Anne, "Les Mesures-étalons de l'abbaye de St.-Denis," *Bulletin monumental*, 137–II, 1979, 141–54.

London, 1932, *Exhibition of French Art (1200–1900)* (exh. cat.), William Clowes and Sons Ltd.

Mâle, Émile, "La Peinture sur verre en France," *Histoire de l'Art...*, André Michel, ed., I, book 2, Paris, 1905, 782–95.

———, "La Part de Suger dans la création de l'iconographie du Moyen Âge," *Revue de l'art ancien et moderne*, XXXV, January–June 1914, 91–102, 161–68, 253–62, 339–49.

Marion du Mersan, T., *Notice des monumens exposés dans le Cabinet des Médailles, antiques et pierres gravées de la Bibliothèque du roi, suivie d'une description des objets les plus curieux que renferme cet établissement*, Paris, 1824.

Marquet de Vasselot, J[ean] J[acques], *Musée du Louvre. Catalogue sommaire de l'orfèvrerie, de l'émaillerie et des gemmes du moyen-âge au XVIIᵉ siècle*, Paris, 1914.

Meulen, Jan van der, "Die Abteikirche von Saint-Denis und die Entwicklung der Frühgotik," *Kunstchronik*, XXX, 2, 1977, 60–61.

Migeon, Gaston, *Manuel d'art musulman II: Les Arts plastiques et industriels*, Paris, 1927.

Molinier, Émile, *Musée National du Louvre. Département des objets d'art du Moyen Âge, de la Renaissance et des temps modernes. Catalogue des ivoires*, Paris, 1896.

———, *Histoire générale des arts appliqués à l'industrie du Vᵉ à la fin du XVIIIᵉ siècle, IV: L'Orfèvrerie religieuse et civile, I: du Vᵉ à la fin du XVᵉ siècle*, Paris, 1902.

Montfaucon, Dom Bernard de, *L'Antiquité expliquée et représentée en figures*, 5 vols. in 10, Paris, 1719.

Montgolfier, Bernard de, and Wilhelm, Jacques, "La Vierge de la famille de Vic," *La Revue des arts*, 5, 1958, 221–28.

Nelson, Philip, "Ancient Painted Glass in England, 1170–1500," *The Antiquary's Book*, London, 1913.

New York, 1930, *Catalogue of an Exhibition of Stained Glass from the XIth to the XVIIIth Century* (exh. cat.), Demotte, Inc.

New York, 1970, *...1200* (exh. cat.), The Metropolitan Museum of Art, Konrad Hoffmann

Oursel, Raymond, "Pierre le Vénérable, Suger et la lumière gothique," *Annales de l'Académie de Mâcon*, XLIV, 1958–59, 53–56.

Panofsky, Erwin, "Note on a Controversial Passage in Suger's 'De Consecratione Ecclesiae Sancti Dionysii,'" *Gazette des Beaux-Arts*, 6th series, XXVI, 1944, 95–114.

———, "Postlogium Sugerianum," *The Art Bulletin*, XXIX, 1947, 119–21.

Paris, 1962, *Cathédrales* (exh. cat.), Musée National du Louvre.

Paris, 1962, *Dix Siècles de joaillerie française* (exh. cat.), Musée National du Louvre.

Paris, 1970–71, *La France de Saint Louis* (exh. cat.), Palais Royal, Salles des gens d'armes du Palais.

Priest, Alan, "The Masters of the West Façade of Chartres," *Art Studies*, I, 1923.

Rackham, Bernard, "English Interpretations of Foreign Stained-Glass in the Early 19th Century," *Journal of the British Society of Master Glass Painters*, II, 2, 1927, 86–94.

————, *Victoria and Albert Museum. Department of Ceramics. A Guide to the Collections of Stained Glass*, London, 1936.

Ricci, Seymour de, "Un Calice du trésor de Saint-Denis," *Comptes-rendus de l'Académie des Inscriptions et Belles-Lettres*, 1923, 335 seq.

Ridder, A[ndré] de, *Catalogue sommaire des bijoux antiques. Musée du Louvre, Département des antiquités grecques et romaines*, Paris, 1924.

Rohault de Fleury, Ch[arles], *La Messe. Études archéologiques sur ses monuments*, 8 vols., Paris, 1883–89.

Schramm, Percy Ernst, and Mütherich, Florentine, *Denkmale der deutschen Könige und Kaiser: ein Beitrag zur Herrschergeschichte von Karl dem Grossen bis Friedrich II, 768–1250*, Munich, 1962.

Sedlmayr, Hans, *Die Entstehung der Kathedrale*, Zurich, 1950.

Seymour, Charles, Jr., *Masterpieces of Sculpture from the National Gallery of Art*, Washington, D.C., 1949.

von Simson, Otto, *Das Mittelalter II: Das hohe Mittelalter* (Propyläen Kunstgeschichte, VI), Berlin, 1972.

Texier, Abbé [Jacques], "Suger, abbé de Saint-Denis," *Dictionnaire d'orfèvrerie, de gravure et de ciselure chrétiennes (Encyclopédie Théologique de Migne)*, XXVII, 3rd ed., Paris, 1857.

Twining, Edward Francis, *A History of the Crown Jewels of Europe*, London, 1960.

————, *European Regalia*, London, 1967.

Vanuxem, Jacques, "The Theories of Mabillon and Montfaucon on French Sculpture of the Twelfth Century," *Journal of the Warburg and Courtauld Institutes*, XX, 1, 1957, 45–58; reprinted in Robert Branner, *Chartres Cathedral*, New York, 1969, 168–85.

Verdier, Philippe, "La Grande Croix de l'abbé Suger à Saint-Denis," *Cahiers de civilisation médiévale, X^e–XIIe siècles*, XIII, 1, January–March 1970, 1–31.

————, "What do we know of the Great Cross of Suger in Saint-Denis," *Gesta*, IX/2, 1970, 12–15.

————, "Suger a-t-il été en France le créateur du thème iconographique du couronnement de la Vierge?," *Gesta*, XV/1–2, 1976, 227–36.

Verlet, Pierre, *La Galerie d'Apollon et ses trésors, Guide sommaire*, Paris, 1947.

Viollet-le-Duc, Eugène-Emmanuel, *Dictionnaire raisonné de l'architecture française du XIe au XVIe siècle*, 10 vols., Paris, 1854–68.

Weisbach, Werner, *Religiöse Reform und mittelalterliche Kunst*, Einsiedeln and Zurich, Switzerland, 1945.

Wells, William, "Some Notes on the Stained Glass in the Burrell Collection in Glasgow Art Gallery," *Journal of the British Society of Master Glass Painters*, XII, 4, 277–80.

Wentzel, Hans, "Unbekannte mittelalterliche Glasmalereien der Burrell Collection zu Glasgow," *Pantheon*, XIX, 1961, 3, May–June, 105–13; 4, July–August, 178–86; 5, September–October, 240–49.

————, "Bergkristall," *Reallexikon zur deutschen Kunstgeschichte II*, 1948, 275–98.

————, "'Staatskameen' im Mittelalter," *Jahrbuch der Berliner Museen*, new series–4, 1962, 42–77.

Index

Numbers in italics refer to pages with illustrations

Photograph Credits